Contents

W9-ARV-771

Biology

Lab Manual

Fourth Edition

Brad R. Batdorf
Elizabeth A. Lacy

bju press®

Greenville, South Carolina

The authors and the publisher have made every effort to ensure that the laboratory exercises in this publication are safe when conducted according to the instructions provided. We assume no responsibility for any injury or damage caused or sustained while performing the activities in this book. Conventional and homeschool teachers, parents, and guardians should closely supervise students who perform the exercises in this manual.

NOTE: The fact that materials produced by other publishers may be referred to in this volume does not constitute an endorsement of the content or theological position of materials produced by such publishers. Any references and ancillary materials are listed as an aid to the student or the teacher and in an attempt to maintain the accepted academic standards of the publishing industry.

BIOLOGY Laboratory Manual
Fourth Edition

Authors
Brad R. Batdorf, MAEd
Elizabeth A. Lacy, MEd

Permissions
Joyce Landis
Sarah Martin

Project Editor
Adelé Hensley

Illustration
John Cunningham

Project Manager
Ted Williams

Page Design
Andrew Fields

Page Layout
Linda Hastie

Cover Design
Elly Kalagayan

Photo credits: © iStockphoto.com/Sascha Burkard (front cover, spine); © iStockphoto.com/Tomasz Zachariasz (back cover); © Carolina Biological/Visuals Unlimited, Inc. ix; BJU Photo Services 13, 14; Biodisc/Visuals Unlimited, Inc. 36 (both); © Dr. John D. Cunningham/Visuals Unlimited, Inc. 39; BJU Photo Services 117; iStockphoto/Thinkstock 167 (left); Kevin Davidson/iStockphoto/Thinkstock 167 (center); Hemera Technologies/Photos.com/Getty Images/Thinkstock 167 (right); Apers0n/Wikipedia/Creative Commons Attribution 2.0 Generic 192

© 2011 BJU Press
Greenville, South Carolina 29609

First Edition (student text) © 1980 BJU Press
First Edition (lab manual) © 1981 BJU Press
Second Edition (both) © 1991 BJU Press
Third Edition (both) © 2005 BJU Press

Printed in the United States of America
All rights reserved

ISBN 978-1-60682-015-5

15 14 13 12 11 10

Handcrafted.

BJU Press employs a team of experienced writers and artists whose best work goes into every book we produce. Because of our emphasis on quality, our textbooks are the top choice in Christian education. Each book is designed to give your student a learning experience that is enjoyable, academically excellent, and biblically sound.

bju **press**®

BECAUSE **IT MATTERS**

To find out more, call **1.800.845.5731** or visit **www.bjupress.com**.

Introduction

Biology can be a bewildering subject. There is a mountain of information, some of it concerning obscure structures and complex processes that take place on an invisible level. Like all science disciplines, it has its own extensive vocabulary seldom used in conversation. Many students become frustrated when they recognize how much there is to learn. At the same time, they see God's wonderful creation all around them. It is impossible to be indifferent to the plants and animals God created. And the processes through which these living things develop and maintain themselves are just as fascinating as the actual organisms are.

Christians have an obligation—set forth in Genesis 1:28—to serve as stewards, or caretakers, of this creation. Effective stewardship depends on knowledge. The laboratory exercises in this manual are designed to provide hands-on exposure to living things from algae and bacteria to mammals. The result should be an increase in knowledge and understanding. While the lab experiences alone will not guarantee comprehension, they should clarify material in the text and make the learning come alive.

It is one thing to read about an object you are not familiar with, listen to a person talk about it, look at pictures of it, and even memorize facts about it. It is quite another matter to actually look at the object, handle it, or do something with it. Sometimes students do not really understand the object being discussed until they become personally familiar with it. It would not be unusual for a high-school biology student to answer correctly every question on a quiz about *Spirogyra* but be surprised to learn that "the stuff in that dish is real *Spirogyra*." The student who has learned all about *Spirogyra* and then has looked at it, placed some on a slide, and examined it through a microscope does not easily forget the "green stringy stuff," even though he may forget its name.

One of the purposes of these laboratory exercises is to provide you with a framework for increasing your understanding of the material. Each exercise is designed to allow you to become personally acquainted with various biological processes and organisms.

A second purpose is to help you study. By asking you to do certain tasks and to answer particular questions (some requiring merely looking up the answer, others requiring thought, and some requiring experimentation), these exercises should help you learn without having to memorize cold facts. It is a well-known educational principle that working with a piece of information not only aids in learning it but also makes it more usable to the learner. This principle lies behind the writing of essays in English class and the working of problems in math class.

Of course, you can learn from your essays and math problems only if you work on them faithfully and carefully.

Otherwise, they become a burden and, for some students, a game to see how few they can do yet still pass the course. These students lose the benefit of these exercises because they have the wrong approach to their work. The same is true of laboratory work in a high-school science course. If you approach it as "something I don't want to do" or as "something that the teacher requires us to do," you will lose many of its benefits. Your attitude toward the laboratory exercises will greatly influence how much you will benefit from them.

The laboratory exercises in this book are designed to go along with *BIOLOGY*. As you cover the material in the *BIOLOGY* textbook (referred to in this manual as the *text*), your teacher will tell you what laboratory exercises (or *labs*) you will be expected to do and when they are to be handed in. A lab is an assignment on which any student, if he is faithful and diligent, can earn a good grade. The teacher will be able to judge the effort you have put forth by looking at how well you did the laboratory exercises. Do your best on them.

Equipment and Safety

The laboratory equipment necessary for doing these exercises will be provided. Some of the basic tools frequently used in the biology laboratory are illustrated and named in Figure 1. Learn the proper names and uses for these tools. Other pieces of equipment (such as the microscope) will be described in the exercises as each piece is needed.

On laboratory days you should be sure to have the following:

- ❏ Your *BIOLOGY* textbook
- ❏ This *BIOLOGY* laboratory manual
- ❏ A binder for holding returned laboratory exercises, unlined white paper for some drawings, and lined loose-leaf paper for taking class notes
- ❏ A pencil and an eraser for laboratory drawings

Beneath the materials lists of some labs are safety icons to alert you to possible dangers. These icons are explained in the box on page viii. When you see a particular symbol in a lab, your teacher should explain to you what the danger is and how to protect yourself.

Working with chemicals sometimes involves certain hazards, such as fire, toxicity, and skin irritation. However, hazards can be minimized by following directions, heeding cautions, and wearing protective equipment such as goggles and aprons when necessary. Working in the laboratory safely is an important skill that you should be learning and practicing during this course. A safe laboratory environment is everyone's responsibility, so be informed!

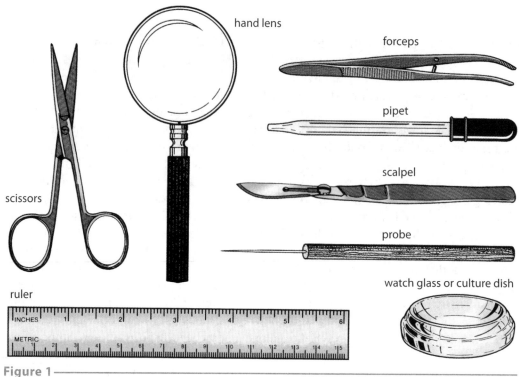

Figure 1
Laboratory equipment

Safety Icons

 Animals Animals that you are to observe or collect may inflict dangerous stings or bites.

 Body protection Chemicals, stains, or other materials could damage your skin or clothing. You should wear a laboratory apron or gloves or both.

 Chemical fumes Chemical fumes may present a danger. Use a chemical fume hood or make sure the area is well ventilated.

 Electricity An electrical device (hot plate, lamp, microscope) will be used. Use the device with care.

 Extreme temperature Extremely hot or cold temperatures may cause skin damage. Use proper tools to handle laboratory equipment.

 Eye protection There is a possible danger to the eyes from chemicals or other materials. Wear safety goggles.

 Fire A heat source or open flame is to be used. Be careful to avoid skin burns and the ignition of combustible materials.

 Gas Improper use of gas can result in burns, explosion, or suffocation. Be careful to check that the gas is turned off when you are finished.

 Pathogens Organisms encountered in the investigation could cause human disease.

 Plants Plants that you are to observe or collect may have sharp thorns or spines or may cause contact dermatitis (inflammation of the skin).

 Poison A substance in the experiment could be poisonous if ingested.

 Sharp objects Cuts are possible from broken glassware (broken test tubes, thermometers, or microscope slides) or sharp instruments (scalpels, razor blades, or knives).

Suppliers of hazardous materials provide Material Safety Data Sheets (MSDS) to accompany their products. These sheets inform the user of the specific hazards involved, the properties of the material, first aid to be administered, protective equipment to be used, waste disposal, and so on. They will be available for immediate reference in the laboratory at all times.

For certain lab days you may also want to bring a protective garment (an old, large shirt to be worn over your school clothes), colored pencils, and hand cream. These pieces of equipment are optional unless your teacher requires them.

Be sure to report all damaged equipment, even if you are not responsible for breaking it. If you are found using a piece of damaged equipment, it may be assumed that you are responsible for breaking the equipment unless you report the damage before you start using it. The policy of your school may be to bill you for such damage or for damage you cause because of carelessness.

Drawings

One of the most common complaints echoing through every high-school biology laboratory is "But I can't draw!" A lack of artistic ability does not have to be a drawback. A good scientific drawing does not require artistic ability as much as it requires a good eye, a steady hand, and a large eraser.

Let's look at some of the reasons for drawing scientific specimens. Making drawings is one of the best ways to learn some of the complex biological structures and processes. If you feel that a drawing is just bothersome busy-work, you will gain little from your drawings. Try a more positive approach. Before attempting a drawing, find out what the text has to say concerning the organism. Look at pictures of the specimen. Then as you draw the specimen, concentrate on its shape, color, function, name, location, and any other characteristics you think of. By the time you have finished, you should *know* it.

Some drawings are meant to be a challenge. You will occasionally be asked to draw something that your text does not discuss. In such cases you will need to consult other texts in order to find enough information to make an intelligent drawing. Students are commonly tempted to try to draw objects they do not understand. Such a drawing will profit little. If you take the time to find the necessary information for yourself, you will not quickly forget what you have worked to achieve.

Students often find themselves copying. They do not actually put a sheet of paper over a picture and trace the object, but they sit with a textbook drawing in front of them and reproduce it without really thinking about what they are drawing. This method can produce a beautiful drawing, but drawings made without concentration and thought bring little profit. For guidance, consult drawings of the specimens you are working on, but never copy the drawings.

Spaces are provided for most of the drawings you will make in these laboratory exercises. Any box with the pencil icon  at the top requires you to draw or label something. A box with the eye icon is for your observation, but it does not require any writing. Occasionally, if you need to begin a drawing again or if you are doing a drawing for which there is not a space, you will need to make a drawing on your own paper. Always use unlined white paper.

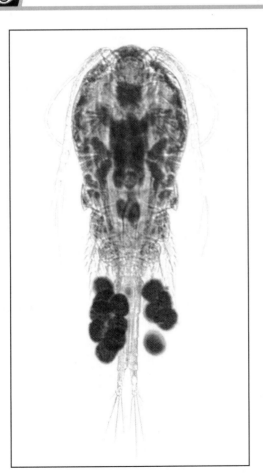

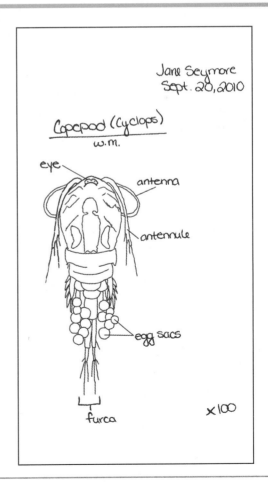

Figure 2
A specimen drawing

Kinds of Scientific Drawings

Within these laboratory exercises you will be asked to do two different types of drawings.

- The **specimen drawing** is made to show exactly what a specimen looks like. It is drawn from an actual specimen, not from a diagram or a picture in a book.
- The **schematic drawing** is often a stylized representation to show a process or a relationship, and therefore it often does not look exactly like the specimen. On page 106 of your text is a group of schematic diagrams that do not look exactly like the photographs beside them, even though they represent the same process. The schematic drawings explain what is taking place in the process being illustrated.

Requirements for a Good Drawing

- Print all information in the same style. Make all printed material parallel with the bottom edge of the paper.
- Put your name in the upper right-hand corner of the drawing. Below your name, put the date the drawing was made. (If you are making your drawing in the spaces provided in this book, your name and the date on the laboratory exercise sheet are sufficient.)
- Center the name of the specimen above the drawing. If the drawing is of a portion of an organism, indicate the portion in the title or under the title. For example, "Fruit fly, leg" indicates that the drawing is of the leg of a fruit fly. The title "Fruit fly" alone indicates a drawing of the entire fly.
- If the specimen has been prepared in some way before being drawn, indicate this under the name of the specimen. (See Methods of Slide Preparation on page xi.)
- Make the drawing large and center it in the space available.
- Do not use shading and color for specimen drawings. Stippling (holding a pencil in a vertical position and tapping the point on the paper) may be used sparingly. In stippling, the dots are all the same size, and a darkened area is obtained by having many dots. Schematic drawings are often made with colored pencils or pens. A colorful drawing should not be a goal in itself, but color may be used if it aids understanding.
- Add labels after the drawing is complete. The label lines should be straight and never cross each other. They should not have arrowheads on them. They should go directly to the object they indicate and touch it or be drawn onto it.
- Label everything that you can identify in the drawing. If you are doing a specimen drawing but do not see some object on your specimen that you know should be there, do not take the liberty of drawing it in. In specimen drawings, draw only what you see in the specimen. In schematic drawings, you may take liberties to aid clarity.
- If you used the microscope, indicate the power in the lower right-hand corner. If you used some other type of magnification (such as a hand lens), write "magnified" or "enlarged" in that corner.
- Do not draw the microscope field or the container the specimen is in.

Normal Laboratory Procedure

Normally, the sequence for completing the laboratory exercises is as follows:

1. The lab day and the day the exercise is due will be announced a few days in advance.

2. Before you come to class each lab day, you are expected to **have read the assigned laboratory exercise completely** and to **have done as much of the work as possible**. Sections or questions in the laboratory exercises that are marked with this symbol can be done without the use of laboratory equipment and can be completed before the lab day or, in a few cases, will need to be done after the lab.

3. On the lab day, you and your laboratory partner will have enough class time to accomplish the work that requires lab equipment if you are prepared and work efficiently. Sometimes answering questions about your work can be done outside of class, allowing you more in-class time to complete the laboratory work.

4. Any sections that you do not finish during the classroom laboratory time become part of your homework. If this requires the use of laboratory equipment, you will need to come to the laboratory at announced make-up times or make arrangements with your teacher to finish the work at some other time.

5. Remove your completed laboratory exercise from this book and staple it together with any materials that the exercise may call for (such as reports or drawings on your own paper), and then hand them in on the date they are due. (This date will generally be several days after the lab day.)

6. The laboratory exercise will be graded and handed back in a few days.

7. Place the returned laboratory exercise in a binder and keep it.

8. The graded labs that are returned to you can be used for test preparation. Be careful not to lose laboratory exercises.

Required / Extra / Omit

When the teacher gives you an assignment, you will need to mark in your laboratory exercise what parts of the assignment your class will be doing. For each section of the exercise, there are boxes like these:

R
E
O

If your teacher tells you that you are expected to do a particular section of the lab, mark box *R* for "required." If your teacher tells you that you may do a section for extra credit, mark box *E* for "extra." If your teacher tells you that you are not to do a section, mark box *O* for "omit."

Methods of Slide Preparation		
Term	**Abbreviation**	**Description**
whole mount	w.m.	slide that contains the entire specimen (e.g., flea) or the entire part of a specimen (e.g., fly leg)
wet mount	w.m.	temporary slide on which the specimen is placed in water
preserved slide		slide on which the specimen is mounted in a medium that permanently keeps the specimen
cross section	c.s. or c.x.	specimen that has been cut crosswise
longitudinal section	l.s. or l.x.	specimen that has been cut lengthwise
teased		specimen that has been shredded into pieces
smeared		specimen that has been smeared across the slide
stained		specimen that has been exposed to dyes in order to color structures

The extra-credit sections will require additional time, and you may have to return to the laboratory after class time. If you are having difficulty with the tests, if your last lab grade was not as good as you had wanted, or if you have been doing poorly on quizzes, you are encouraged to do some of the extra-credit sections to gain points. If you are doing well in the course, you should do an extra-credit section only if it sounds exceptionally interesting. Extra-credit sections must be done before the laboratory exercise is handed in; they may not be done at the end of the course to improve your grade.

Late Laboratory Work

Points will be deducted from the score of a laboratory exercise for each day it is late. Normally, laboratory exercises will not be accepted if they are more than three days late. If you experience unusual difficulties, talk to your teacher to see whether an exception can be made.

When living organisms are used in a laboratory exercise, you usually must immediately make up any lab work that you miss. The organisms may not be available for an extended time.

Conduct and Honor System

Some of the materials and tools used in the laboratory are extremely dangerous if they are misused. For this reason, **do not engage in horseplay at any time**. Horseplay is any use of any piece of laboratory equipment for a purpose other than that for which it was intended. Your teacher will impose severe penalties if you commit this offense.

Do your own work for this class. Do not obtain answers from other students or their work. This is cheating. Your teacher may allow students to help each other by discussing the material and sharing sources of information, but you should never tell each other the answers or copy each other's work. Handing in your laboratory exercise is your statement that you have not cheated. If you have difficulties, see your instructor for help. Occasionally, your teacher may give you special permission to use someone else's data as a source when you are making up work.

Tips for Preparing Laboratory Work

- **Mark the drawings you need to make** when you read the laboratory exercise before coming to class. Then check them off as you finish them.
- **Note carefully what you did wrong** when you receive a graded lab, and do not make the same mistakes again. For example, if you are told that your label lines are sloppy on your first drawings, use a ruler to draw the lines on other drawings.
- **Follow carefully the instructions** given in the laboratory exercise. They will usually answer your questions. Most of the points you miss on a lab will be for either not doing a section or not following directions carefully.
- **The subpoints under a larger point pertain to the larger point.** Since the subpoints usually explain or give more detailed instructions, be sure to read all the subpoints before you begin work.
- **Do what you can at home** either before you come to class on lab day or after lab day (but before the laboratory exercise is due).
- **Consult your text for material concerning your laboratory work.** If the laboratory exercise tells you to read certain pages in the text, do so. Coming to a lab day unprepared to do a laboratory exercise is a waste of time. Do your best to know what you are doing.

1a The Scientific Method

Introduction

While looking in the newspaper for an article for history class, Laura read a report about the amount of time some teenagers spend using handheld gaming devices. The article stated that this activity has increased greatly in the last generation and further stated that some believe that use of these devices increases eye-hand coordination. She began to wonder whether there is some simple way to measure eye-hand coordination.

Laura looked through her textbook and learned that what we see is perceived by light waves entering the eye. These are processed by the retina, which then transmits electrical impulses through the optic nerve to the brain's primary visual center. This information is then passed to the brain's primary motor area, which stimulates muscle movement by transmitting an impulse down the spinal cord to the appropriate muscles. This same process helps you pick up your dinner plate or throw your hands up to avoid being hit in the face by a foul ball.

Because Laura did not have a stopwatch but wanted a consistent way to measure response time, she decided to use a falling meter stick. The test subject would have to catch the falling meter stick after seeing it begin to fall. The distance it fell before being stopped would indirectly measure the response time.

🏠 Preliminary Work

Your class will suggest experiments dealing with eye-hand coordination, choose a problem, design and conduct an experiment to supply data that can be used to determine an answer to the problem, and arrive at a conclusion. For this experiment you may use only a meter stick. (Of course, you should also have a pencil, paper, and other classroom materials.) Before you come to class, devise a few problems about eye-hand coordination that you consider interesting and that the class could experiment with. Complete the material below before you come to class so that you can suggest a possible experiment.

I. List several problems dealing with eye-hand coordination that could be used in class.

- Be sure your problems are worded as questions that have limitations and can be answered with yes, no, or a number.

- Avoid problems that might involve danger (e.g., dropping a meter stick toward someone's face) or those you would not be able to test (such as comparing red-haired people with blond-haired people when you have only one red-haired person in your class).

Goals
✓ Devise a problem that can be solved using the scientific method
✓ Devise an experiment that will supply data to determine an answer to the problem
✓ Collect and interpret data
✓ Learn the steps of the scientific method

Materials
meter stick

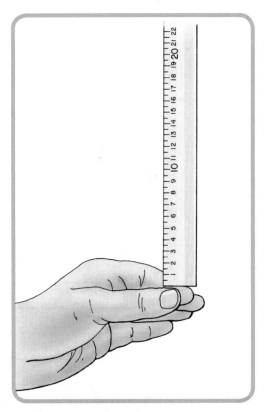

1a-1
An illustration of Laura's test for eye-hand coordination. The tester releases the meter stick; then the test subject must close his fingers as quickly as possible to catch the falling meter stick. Measurements on the meter stick will then indicate not an actual time, but the distance the stick dropped before it was stopped by the finger closure.

- List possible problems for the experiment.

  _____

  _____

  _____

  _____

II. Develop the problem you consider the best one by answering the following questions.

- Choose a problem that can be tested scientifically.

  _____

  _____

- State a hypothesis for this problem.

  _____

  _____

- Describe the steps of an experiment that will supply data to either support or contradict your hypothesis. (Attach additional paper if necessary.)

  _____

  _____

  _____

  _____

  _____

  □ What is your independent variable (single variable)?

  _____

  □ What is your dependent variable?

  _____

  □ List your *standardized* variables. These are the variables that you keep the same in all the treatments so that the change in the dependent variable will be a result of the independent variable.

  _____

  _____

  _____

  _____

  _____

  □ What is serving as your control group?

  _____

  □ What results would you expect if your hypothesis is supported? Rejected?

  _____

  _____

  _____

  _____

In-Class Procedures

At the beginning of the laboratory period, the class will choose a problem suggested by one of its members. As a group you will then devise an experiment and determine exactly how it will be conducted. The class will then divide into groups and conduct the experiment. Results of the experiment will be recorded on a chart and will be interpreted on the following day. As the class decides which problems to use and devises the experiment to conduct, record this information in the spaces below. (Use additional paper if necessary.)

I. Our problem is

_____

II. Our hypothesis is

_____

III. Our experiment involves

_____

_____

- Our independent variable is

_____

- Our dependent variable is

_____

- What are the standardized variables? The steps taken to limit the variables include

_____

_____

_____

_____

_____

_____

_____

- Our procedure for the experiment is

_____

_____

_____

_____

_____

_____

_____

_____

_____

_____

- My observations of problems encountered while conducting the experiment include

_____

_____

_____

_____

IV. Record the results and create a bar graph. Review how to create graphs in Appendix A.

Conclusions

The day following the experiment, the class will interpret the data obtained. After your in-class discussion, answer the following questions.

I. Data analysis

- Create a bar graph using the class data. How does the class graph compare to your graph?

_____

- What conclusions can be drawn from the data?

_____

- Does the data tend to support the hypothesis?   ☐ yes   ☐ no

II. Personal observations

- Were limitations to the problem and controls on the experiment enough to supply reliable data?   ☐ yes   ☐ no
- What could you have done to improve the limitations and controls?

_____

_____

_____

- Can you think of any additional changes that need to be made?

_____

_____

_____

- Was the experiment repeated often enough to give reliable data?   ☐ yes   ☐ no
- How often would be enough to give reliable data?

_____

- Based upon your experience, what other experiments dealing with eye-hand coordination would you like to try?

_____

Inquiry Investigation

Use the steps of the scientific method to determine which type of paper airplane flies the farthest. Define the problem, state the hypothesis, set up the experimental variables and procedures, collect data, and analyze results.

1b The Microscope

Introduction

As you study biology, you will need various pieces of equipment to test, measure, or observe living things. The microscope is probably the most useful, as well as one of the most technical, pieces of equipment found in the average high-school laboratory. Because of the knowledge that can be obtained by using a modern microscope, today's biology student is frequently better informed in some aspects of biological knowledge than the professional biologist of one hundred years ago.

The microscope is a precision instrument that uses magnification and light refraction to produce an enlarged image. Though durable and easy to handle, the microscope requires proper care. Since repairing or replacing this piece of equipment is expensive, every biology student needs to know how its parts function and how to operate it correctly.

The Structure of a Microscope

Identify and label the parts of the microscope on Figure 1b-1. You should be thoroughly familiar with the terms and be able to locate each part on a standard microscope in your classroom.

I. The mechanical parts

- **Body tube:** This long, narrow tube runs half the length of the microscope. The observer looks into one end, and the specimen is placed under the other end. The fixed separation allows the lenses to remain the proper distance apart during viewing. In those microscopes with an inclined body tube, mirrors are used to bend the path of the image.

- **Revolving nosepiece:** A movable disc at the bottom of the body tube allows the interchanging of different sets of lenses (objectives).

- **Coarse adjustment knobs:** There is a large knob on each side of the microscope, usually located directly behind the body tube. These knobs provide substantial movement of the body tube and quick focusing of the specimen.

- **Fine adjustment knobs:** Usually small, these knobs are found underneath the coarse adjustment knobs. Occasionally, they are centered on the coarse adjustment knobs. By providing slight movement of the body tube, the fine adjustment produces a sharper focus.

- **Arm:** The "backbone" of the microscope supports the body tube.

- **Base:** The large rectangular or horseshoe-shaped structure at the bottom of the microscope supports the microscope and keeps it steady.

- **Stage:** A platform positioned directly below the objectives and above the mirror or light source supports the specimen.

- **Stage clips:** The fastenings on top of the stage hold the slide containing the specimen firmly in place.

Goals

✓ Identify the basic parts of the microscope

✓ Demonstrate how to operate a microscope properly

✓ Become familiar with the theory of magnification

✓ Draw a scientific diagram

Materials

microscope
lens paper
tissue
preserved slide of desmids or diatoms
illuminator (optional)
immersion oil
2 hand lenses
preserved slide of colored threads

II. The optical parts

- **Eyepiece or ocular:** Located at the top of the body tube, the eyepiece contains lenses that help increase magnification of the specimen.

- **Objectives:** Two or three metal cylinders extend from the bottom of the revolving nosepiece and contain lenses that produce different magnifications.

- **Diaphragm:** Located between the stage and the light source, the diaphragm regulates the amount of light that passes through the specimen. (Two types of diaphragms are the iris diaphragm, which opens and closes like the iris of an eye, and the disc diaphragm, which is a disc with holes of various sizes.)

- **Substage condenser:** Also located between the stage and the light source, this lens system affects the microscope's resolution by bending and concentrating light before it reaches the specimen. (Some microscopes do not have one.)

- **Light source:** Found on or just above the base, the light source sends light up through the stage and through the specimen. Some microscopes have a mirror instead of an electric light source.

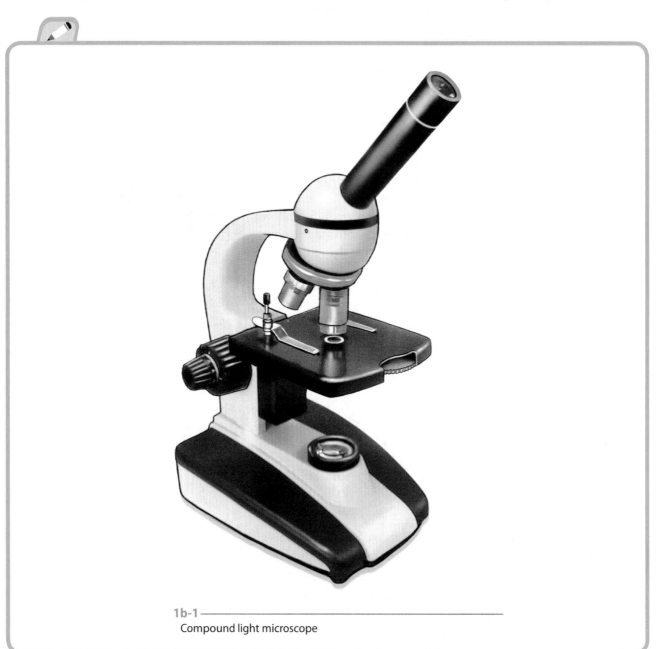

1b-1 ——————————————————
Compound light microscope

How to Care for a Microscope

I. Carry the microscope properly. Excessive jars and bumps may knock the lenses out of adjustment.

- Do not bump the microscope against the sides of the cabinet when removing or returning it.
- Carry the microscope with two hands, one under the base and the other on the arm.
- Be sure to keep the microscope close to your body in an upright position so that the ocular does not slip out of the body tube.
- Place the microscope gently on the table at least three inches from the edge.

II. Prepare the microscope properly. Your microscope may need to be cleaned before you begin to use it.

- Use lens paper to clean lens surfaces and the mirror.
- Wipe the lens in one direction across the diameter of the lens.
- Dust on the lens may be ground in if you use a circular motion and may scratch the lens.
- Consult your instructor if any material remains on your objectives. You may need to use a solvent to remove the material. Never use your fingernail or another object to chip away hardened material.
- Under no circumstances should you attempt to take your microscope apart.

III. Return the microscope properly. When returning a microscope after you have used it, be sure to follow this routine:

- Adjust the microscope (if necessary) so that the body tube is straight up and down.
- Remove the slide from the stage.
- Put the low-power objective directly under the body tube.
- Adjust the body tube to its lowest position.
- Carefully return the microscope to the place where you obtained it.
- Cover the microscope with a dust cover if one is available.

How to Obtain an Image with a Microscope

To observe the specimens clearly and easily, you will need to follow carefully the procedures discussed in this section. After you have done these procedures a few times, they will become second nature, and you will be able to do them quickly. Some of the procedures, such as computing the powers of your microscope, will need to be done only once; others will need to be done every time you focus on a new specimen. Carefully note all the procedures. If difficulties arise, review these instructions and make sure you have not missed something. Of course, if you have any difficulty, your instructor can help you.

I. Compute the powers available on your microscope.

- You are able to see organisms many times larger than their actual size because of the microscope's magnifying powers. Each increase in power reveals a closer look at the specimen.
- You will find numbers that represent powers written on the parts of the microscope that have magnifying lenses. Power in this case refers to the number of times larger the magnified object will appear. Therefore, the total magnification is the product of the magnifying powers of both the ocular and the objective lenses. (Be sure to use only the power of the objective that is directly above the specimen when computing the total power of your microscope. The other objectives are not in use until they are placed over the specimen.)
- Using the powers and other information found on your microscope, fill in the chart on page 8.

Computing the Magnification of a Microscope

Place the power (number of times it magnifies) of each part of your microscope in the proper space and then compute the total magnification for each objective.

	Ocular		Objective		Total Magnification
Low-power objective	_____ ×	times	_____ ×	=	_____ ×
High-power objective	_____ ×	times	_____ ×	=	_____ ×
Oil-immersion objective	_____ ×	times	_____ ×	=	_____ ×
Other	_____ ×	times	_____ ×	=	_____ ×

(Some microscopes do not have an oil-immersion objective; if yours does not, omit that line of the chart. If your microscope has other objectives, include them on separate lines.)

- Answer the following:
  - Why should the substage condenser not be included in computing the magnification?

    _____

  - What advantage does the substage condenser provide to viewing the specimen?

    _____

II. Obtain the proper light in your microscope.

- You must have proper lighting for optimal use of your microscope.
  - Begin by opening the diaphragm so that it admits as much light as possible. Look under the stage to see if the diaphragm is open completely.
    - To adjust an iris diaphragm, move the tiny lever located under the stage forward or backward.
    - To adjust a disc diaphragm, rotate the dial until the largest hole is properly aligned.
  - If your microscope has a built-in light source, simply plug it in and turn the switch on.
  - If your microscope has a mirror, adjust it to provide adequate lighting.
    - Natural light (sunlight) is best, but not direct sunlight, which could damage your eye, leaving a permanent afterimage. An illuminator may be used with a mirror for more consistent lighting.
    - Make sure no object comes between the mirror of your microscope and the light source.
    - Use the curved rather than the flat side of the mirror to obtain an even, unobscured circle of light that fills your field of vision.
    - Look through the eyepiece and adjust the mirror.
- Normally we see light that reflects from an object or light that radiates from something such as a candle flame. In a microscope, however, light is reflected from the mirror and passes through the lenses to our eyes. How are we able to see a specimen placed on the stage of the microscope when no light is reflected from the specimen?

  _____

  _____

III. Position the specimen.

- Obtain a preserved slide of either diatoms or desmids.

Microscope Slides

The specimen is usually mounted on a glass slide and covered with a cover slip.

- Be sure the slide is clean before you use it. Prepared or preserved slides (those professionally made) may be cleaned with a tissue or lens paper. Do not scratch the slide.

- Unless already noted on the label of the slide, all cracks or damage should be reported to your instructor.

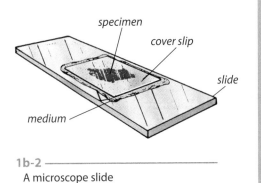

1b-2 ——————————
A microscope slide

- Place the slide on the stage, directly over the opening in the stage.
  - □ Make sure that the cover slip is on top, or you will have trouble focusing.
  - □ Place the stage clips on both ends of the slide (but not on the cover slip) to hold the slide in place.
- Position the slide so that the specimen is centered in the opening of the stage.
  - □ To move the slide on the stage, place your thumbs on opposite corners of the slide and push or pull the slide into position.
  - □ Use dry slides on the stage of a microscope. If the lower surface of the slide is wet, it tends to form a suction that makes the slide very difficult to move and may cause damage.

IV. Focus the microscope on low power.

- Focus your microscope, following these steps:
  1. Raise the body tube using the coarse adjustment knob and move the 10× objective clockwise until it fits directly below the body tube. You should hear a click when the objective reaches the correct position.
  2. Looking at your microscope from the side, turn the coarse adjustment knob to move the body tube down toward the stage. Stop when the objective is just above the slide. (Some microscopes have safety devices that will stop the body tube automatically.)
  3. Look into the ocular and carefully move the body tube up slowly until the specimen is brought into view. (The body tube usually moves up when the coarse adjustment knob is turned toward you; however, look into the ocular while moving it.) (NOTE: Never turn the coarse adjustment knob so that the body tube goes down while you look in the eyepiece. You may damage the slide or lens.)
  4. Now use the fine adjustment knob to get sharper images. One turn in either direction is usually enough to focus properly. Do not spin the knob; you could damage the mechanism.
  5. If no image comes into view by the time you have moved the objective one inch from the cover slip, you probably
     - ♦ Tried to focus too fast and passed the point of focus. Start at number 2 above and try again.
     - ♦ Did not have a specimen in your field of view. Check to make sure there is something on the slide directly in the center of the hole in the stage. Then try again.
     - ♦ Have too much light. Use a slightly smaller opening of your diaphragm and try again.
  6. If you still cannot obtain an image, ask your instructor for help.
- Note some of the effects of using the light microscope.
  - □ If you move the slide to the right, how does the position of the material change in your field of view?

    □ Turn the fine adjustment knob slowly to move the objective up or down. Describe what happens to the image you are viewing.

_____

_____

V. Prepare a specimen drawing of desmids or diatoms. Follow these instructions:

- Draw five specimens in Area A using the instructions provided in the Introduction (pp. ix–x).
- You may obtain all the specimens from one slide. Draw desmids or diatoms, whichever you are looking at.
- Make sure you are drawing typical specimens, not just odd globs you find on your slide.
- These specimens have been preserved and stained; they will not appear green as the ones in your text do.
- For this set of drawings, draw only the outlines of your specimens. Ignore the internal structures.

How to Use High Power on Your Microscope

I. Observe a desmid or diatom using high power (400×–450×).

- Center the desmid or diatom of your choice in your microscope field. Why is it essential to position the specimen in the center?

_____

_____

_____

- Focus your microscope first on low power, and then go to high power, following these instructions:
    - □ On the nosepiece of most microscopes are several objectives. Most modern microscopes are parfocal: if a microscope is focused on a specimen using one power, all the objectives will be nearly in focus for that specimen (unless the specimen is exceptionally thick). Most parfocal microscopes can be focused on a higher power with only a 1/4 turn of the fine adjustment knob.

A

B

□ All you need to do to change a parfocal microscope to high power (about 400×–450×, but not oil-immersion power, which is about 1000×) is rotate the nosepiece.

□ While you do so, look at the stage from the side to be sure that the objective does not touch the slide as it clicks into place.

II. Prepare a specimen drawing of a section of a desmid or diatom in Area B, including the internal structures.

How to Use the Oil-Immersion Power on Your Microscope

I. Follow these procedures carefully when using oil-immersion objectives.

- Be sure you have a very bright light source. An illuminator is usually necessary for a microscope with a mirror.

- Following the procedures given earlier, focus on low power and then on high power.

- Make sure that what you wish to observe is in the center of the microscope field.

- Turn the nosepiece half a turn toward the oil-immersion objective.

- Place one small drop of immersion oil on the slide.

    □ The drop should be centered on the cover slip.

    □ Do not get oil on the label of the slide.

- Turn the nosepiece so that the oil-immersion objective (96×–100×) is down and touches the drop of oil. Make sure to watch from the side so that the objective doesn't hit the slide.

- Adjust the tube so that the objective continues to touch the drop of oil. Observing from the side, continue adjustment until the objective almost touches the slide.

- Observing through the microscope, adjust the tube very slowly until focus is obtained. The fine adjustment knob is best for this purpose and usually needs to be turned less than one full rotation.

- If the objective is raised so high that the oil separates from the objective, you have passed the point of focus. Repeat the two preceding steps.

- Focus problems often result from too much light. Adjust the diaphragm.

- If the object was centered when you focused using the lower powers, it will be centered under oil-immersion power. If it is not, carefully move the slide to the correct position.

- When you finish, clean the microscope and the slide carefully, following these steps:

    1. Remove excess oil from the slide and objective with a dry tissue.

    2. Clean the slide with a wet tissue, being careful not to wet the label. Dry the slide thoroughly before returning it.

    3. Clean the objective thoroughly with a wet tissue. Pat it dry with a dry tissue.

    4. Polish the objective with lens paper.

II. Using oil-immersion power, observe a desmid or diatom and draw a portion of the specimen in Area C. Include the internal structures.

C

How a Microscope Works

Microscopes work because light bends as it passes through substances of different densities. However, the higher the magnification is, the more difficulties are encountered with resolution and depth of focus. An understanding of these problems is necessary for good microscope use.

I. Reverse image

- Observe what happens to light rays that are reflected from this paper when they pass through hand lenses by doing the following:

  □ Hold two hand lenses, one on top of the other, about four inches from the paper.

  □ Hold your head about fourteen inches from the hand lenses.

  □ Focus by moving your head.

- Explain why the image is inverted. You may use diagrams if necessary.

_____

_____

1b-3
Two hand lenses

II. Problems with increasing magnification and depth of focus

- Using low power, focus on a slide of three intersecting threads.

  □ Why is the intersection of the three threads black?

_____

  □ By adjusting the focus, you should be able to see all of a thread clearly.

- Observe the intersection of the three threads on high power, following these steps:

  □ With the microscope on low power, move the slide so that the intersection of the three threads is in the exact center of your field of view.

  □ Focus your microscope on high power. Now that you have changed powers, note the different size of the black spot in the center of the junction of the three threads.

  ♦ Adjust the position of your slide until all three threads are visible.

  ♦ You probably will not be able to see all three threads at once because they are stacked and you have limited depth of focus while using high power.

  ♦ Using the fine adjustment knob, determine the sequence of threads at the intersection. From top to bottom, they are

_____

  □ Although higher powers of the light microscope allow you to see more detail, they present other difficulties. What are they?

_____

_____

2 Osmosis

Introduction

Cells are dependent upon water being able to move in and out through the selectively permeable membrane that surrounds them. Osmosis, the movement of water across a semipermeable membrane, is a quantifiable process. In this exercise you will explore how solute concentrations affect water movement though semipermeable membranes that separate various solutions. The data will be collected, and you will then form a conclusion about osmosis.

Goals

✓ Observe a demonstration of osmosis

✓ Apply the steps of the scientific method

✓ Predict how various factors affect the rate of osmosis

✓ Interpret data and draw conclusions about osmosis

A Demonstration of Osmosis

I. Preliminary work

- Research question:

    _____

    _____

    _____

- Hypothesis:

    _____

    _____

    _____

II. The experimental setup

- Prepare the bags of solution.

    ▫ Obtain 3 strips of dialysis tubing that have been soaked in distilled water.

    ▫ Close one end of each strip with a clamp. This will form a bag with an open end.

    ▫ Solutions A, B, and C will be placed into separate dialysis bags by placing 10 mL of solution in each bag with a pipet.

    ▫ Solution A: 10 mL of sucrose solution A

    Solution B: 10 mL of sucrose solution B

    Solution C: 10 mL of distilled water

    There are two different concentrations of sucrose. Solution B contains twice as much sugar as solution A.

    ▫ Clamp the other end of the tubing, leaving a 2 cm pocket of air. Label the clamp with the letter of the solution in the bag.

    ▫ Rinse each of the bags with distilled water and blot dry with a paper towel.

    ▫ Measure the mass of each bag and record the data.

- Prepare the beakers.

    ▫ Label the beakers A, B, and C.

    ▫ Fill the beakers with distilled water.

Materials

3 strips of dialysis tubing

distilled water

6 clamps

sucrose solutions

pipet

wax pencil

balance

3 beakers

timer

2-1
Solution being added to dialysis bag

- Run the experiment.
  - ▢ Place the bags in the corresponding beakers (e.g., bag A should be in beaker A) at the same time.
  - ▢ Allow each of the solutions to soak for 5 minutes.
  - ▢ At the end of 5 minutes, take all of the bags out of the water at the same time.
  - ▢ Dry the bags COMPLETELY with a paper towel and determine their mass.
  - ▢ Record the masses of the bags in the data table.
  - ▢ Replace the bags in the water. Continue taking measurements every 5 minutes for 30 minutes.

2-2
Dialysis bags in distilled water

III. Identify the variables in this experiment.
  - Independent variable:

  _____

  - Dependent variable:

  _____

  - Standardized variables:

  _____

  _____

  _____

  _____

  - Control group:

  _____

  _____

  _____

IV. Predict the results.

- What results do you expect if your hypothesis is supported? Falsified?

_____

_____

_____

_____

- Use arrows to draw the predicted direction of net water movement for each of the bags in Figure 2-3.

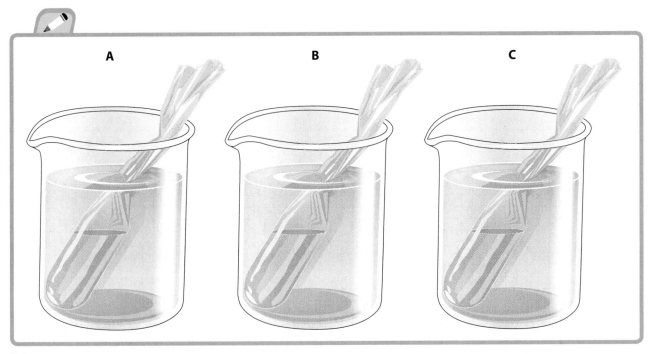

2-3
Direction of osmosis

V. Record your results.

- Record the mass of the bags in the table below. Determine the percent change (% change) for each time by the following formula: [(final mass – initial mass)/initial mass] × 100% = % change.

- Draw a line graph showing the % change on the *y*-axis and the change in time on the *x*-axis. Plot each of the three solutions separately but on the same graph.

	Start	5 min.	10 min.	15 min.	20 min.	25 min.	30 min.	Total change
Mass solution A (mL)								
% change solution A								
Mass solution B (mL)								
% change solution B								
Mass solution C (mL)								
% change solution C								

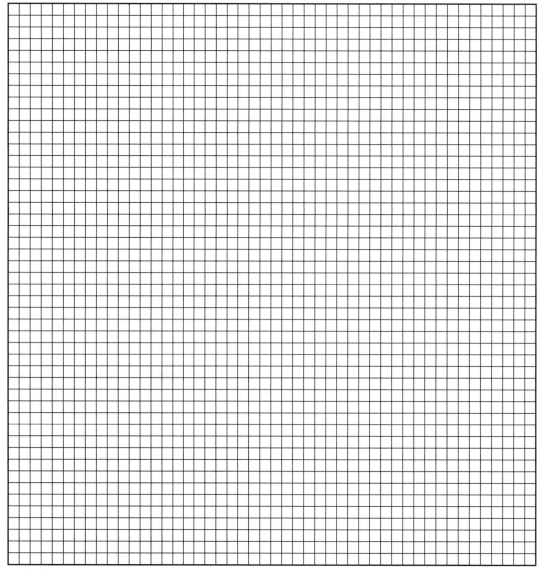

🏠 *Conclusions*

Carefully read the following discussions in your text: diffusion and osmosis, pages 41, 43, and 45; catalysts and enzymes, pages 39–40; and sugars, pages 47–48.

I. Analyze your results in terms of your graph.

_____

_____

_____

_____

II. Do the data support your hypothesis? Explain using specific results.

_____

_____

III. From the results of the experiment, what can you conclude about the permeability of the membrane to sucrose?

_____

IV. Was there a difference between the increase in mass of the bag with solution A compared to the bag with solution B? ☐ yes ☐ no   If so, what would account for the difference?

_____

_____

_____

V. Use your data to answer the research question.

_____

VI. If you let the experiment run long enough, could all of the water from the beaker enter the bag? Why or why not?

_____

_____

_____

VII. If you slowly heated the water in either beaker, what might happen to the rate of osmosis and why?

_____

_____

VIII. If you set up the dialysis bags using salt instead of sucrose, would you expect similar results? Why or why not?

_____

_____

_____

IX. What factors could have affected your results?

_____

X. Our cells are surrounded by a selectively permeable membrane. What would happen if our cells were placed in a container of distilled water?

_____

_____

XI. Sucrase is an enzyme that breaks down the disaccharide sucrose to two monosaccharides. The monosaccharides can diffuse through the semipermeable membrane of the dialysis tubing. Predict how the enzyme would affect the sugar molecule and water movement if added to the bag.

_____

_____

_____

_____

_____

Research Question

How does the factor of temperature affect the rate of osmosis?

Design an experiment through the steps of the scientific method to test how temperature affects osmosis using the technique you learned in this lab.

3a Basic Cytology

Introduction

In your biological studies, you will need to know how to prepare a wet mount, a temporary microscope slide in which the specimen is mounted in water or some other fluid. After you have read about how to prepare a wet mount, you will practice the technique by doing what Hooke did to observe for the first time what he called cells.

Cells are the basic structural and functional units of all living organisms. Whether an organism is microscopic and single celled (like an amoeba or a bacterium) or multicellular (like your body), a study of an organism's cells is important.

Cells from both plants and animals can be easily studied in the laboratory. The onion will represent plants for this laboratory exercise. Though it may appear dead, the onion is a living bulb that produces roots and leaves when planted. The cells in the lining of your own mouth will represent living "animal" cells.

Goals

✓ Prepare a wet mount using correct technique

✓ Identify cell walls on a wet mount slide of a plant cell

✓ Stain and identify a plant and an animal cell

✓ Describe the similarities and differences between plant and animal cells

Materials

cork stopper
large hexagonal metal nut
single-edged razor blade
glass slides
cover slips
microscope
onion
dissection kit
methylene blue
flat toothpick

How to Prepare a Wet Mount

I. Preparing the slides and cover slips

- Hold glass slides and cover slips by their edges so that you do not leave fingerprints on them.

- Thoroughly rinse a glass slide and a cover slip by following these instructions:

  □ Be careful not to bend plastic cover slips. If you are using a glass cover slip, handle it gently; splinters from shattered glass cover slips easily enter the fingers and may require surgical removal.

  □ Inspect plastic cover slips for any excessive scratches. If too many scratches appear, discard the cover slip.

  □ Use only water when washing the slides and cover slips. Soap film may kill or damage living specimens. If you cannot clean your slide completely by rinsing it in water, take it to your instructor and obtain another slide.

- Thoroughly dry the slide.

  □ Shake excess water into the sink.

  □ Blot the slide and cover slip with a paper towel.

  □ Finish drying with a soft tissue.

- Set the glass slide and the cover slip on the edge of a book or table so that you can pick them up by the edges without getting fingerprints on them.

3a-1
Handling glass slides

II. Mounting the specimen

- Place the specimen on the slide by following one of these techniques.

  □ *If the specimen is small (unicellular or colonial) and already in a fluid medium,* use a pipet to place a single drop of the specimen-containing medium on the center of the slide.

  □ *If the specimen is large (a tissue or a clump of organisms),* follow these steps:

    1. Using a pipet, place a small drop of water (or culture medium) on the slide.

    2. Using forceps, place the specimen in the drop of water. In some cases, your teacher may provide a special concavity slide that has a shallow "well" to hold larger specimens.

    3. If necessary, prepare (smear or tease) the specimen.

    4. If the specimen remains dry on top, place another drop of water (or culture medium) on top of the specimen.

3a-2
Preparing a wet mount

- Place the cover slip on top of the specimen by following these instructions:

  □ Place the cover slip so that one edge is touching the slide and the cover slip is held at a 45° angle above the drop of water.

  □ Slowly lay the cover slip down on top of the water and specimen.

  □ If bubbles appear in the area you are going to view, tap the cover slip with the tip of a probe to remove the bubbles.

  □ If too many bubbles appear, take the wet mount apart and start again.

  □ If you have used too much water, you may need to blot dry the bottom of the slide before placing it on the microscope stage. You may also need to remove excess water from around the cover slip by lightly touching a paper towel to the water. Absorption will remove the water.

III. Cleaning up and putting away the wet mount

- When you finish observing the slide, remove the cover slip and specimen. When a stain is used, remove the cover slip with forceps.

  □ If the specimen is microscopic in size, rinse it down the drain.

  □ If the specimen is large (a tissue or clump of organisms), wrap it in a paper towel and put the paper towel in the trash can.

- Rinse the slide and cover slip in running water.

- Shake the excess water into the sink.

- Place the slides and cover slips in the places provided.

  □ You do not need to dry the slide and cover slip completely.

  □ Do **not** stack the wet slides or cover slips. When dry, they will be impossible to separate.

Cork Cells

Over three hundred years ago Robert Hooke discovered that certain plant tissues are made up of what he called "cells." To get a proper perspective of cytology, you will repeat his experiment. To see cork cells well, you must use a very thin slice of cork only one to two cells thick. If suitable slices of cork are provided for you, begin at Section II below. If you must cut your own, begin at Section I.

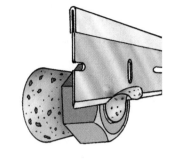

3a-3 —————
Slicing cork

I. Cut a sliver of cork by following these instructions:

- Take a small cork stopper (piece of cork) and insert it into a hexagonal metal nut.

   □ Twist it carefully so that the flat surface of the cork does not become crooked inside the nut.

   □ As the cork reaches the other side, continue to turn it until it barely protrudes beyond the nut.

- Run a single-edged razor blade along the surface of the nut, carefully cutting into the cork. You do not need to get an entire cross section of the cork, but the section you use must be very thin.

II. Prepare a wet mount of cork by following these instructions:

- Pick up your cork slice carefully (it may crumble) and position it on top of the water of your wet mount.

- Add another drop of water on top of the cork slice before putting on the cover slip.

- If your cover slip "teeter-totters" on the cork, your slice of cork is too thick. Start again.

III. Observe the wet mount of cork on low power.

- Your slice is probably thinnest along one of the edges, so you might want to start exploring there first.

- When you observe wet mounts, remember that the microscope stage must remain parallel to the floor. Why is this necessary?

   _____

- Can you see any internal cellular structures in the cork cells?   ☐ yes ☐ no   Explain.

   _____

- You are, of course, observing dead cork. What cellular structure are you observing?

   _____

Onion Epidermal Cells

I. Observe onion epidermal cells.

- Obtain the scale of a small onion.

   □ A scale is one of the layers of the onion.

   □ The thin, translucent skin on the inside surface of the scale is the epidermis of the onion.

- Remove a layer of onion epidermis by following these instructions:

   □ Take the scale and break it. At the edges of the broken scale, you should be able to see a portion of the epidermis.

   □ Peel a translucent layer from the scale using your forceps. *Translucent* means it allows light through but is not transparent.

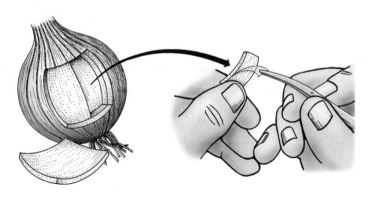

3a-4 —————
Removing the onion epidermis

▫ The epidermis is a very thin sheet of cells, so do not crush or wrinkle it. Otherwise, cells become damaged and air bubbles get trapped between the layers, making it hard to observe.

- Prepare a wet mount, using a small piece of onion epidermis no larger than the drop of water on your slide.

    ▫ Place the onion epidermis so that it lies flat. If it begins to fold or curl, use probes to straighten it.

    ▫ Put the second drop of water on it and then put the cover slip on. The cover slip should adhere tightly. If it appears to be floating, you can draw some water off with a paper towel. If there are large air bubbles, then there is not enough water and you can add small amounts with a pipet at the edge of the cover slip. You may need your lab partner's help.

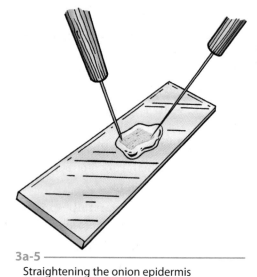

3a-5 —
Straightening the onion epidermis

- Observe the onion epidermis cells under low power.

    ▫ What is the general shape of one onion epidermal cell? _____

    Of a group? _____

    ▫ What do the cork and onion cells have in common? _____

    _____

    ▫ Mark the terms that apply to the onion epidermis:

    ☐ unicellular   ☐ multicellular   ☐ tissue   ☐ organ   ☐ system

II. Stain your onion epidermal cells and observe them again.

- Stain the cells by following these steps:

    ▫ Carefully remove the slide from the stage and place it next to the microscope.

    ▫ Place one drop of methylene blue on the slide at the very edge of the cover slip, in contact with the water under the cover slip. At the opposite side, touch a paper towel to the water under the edge of the cover slip, allowing the paper to absorb the water. The stain will be drawn under the cover slip. (If the stain runs over the outside edges of the cover slip, you probably used too much water when you made your wet mount. Use paper towels to absorb the excess water and try again.)

    ▫ When the stain has contacted the onion epidermis, blot away any excess fluids on the slide or cover slip.

    ▫ Allow the stain to remain on the slide three to five minutes before observing the specimen. This permits the stain to enter the cells. If you don't see changes after five minutes, you may need to add another drop of stain or wait a little longer.

3a-6 —
Staining cells in a wet mount

- Observe the stained onion epidermis on low and on high power.

    ▫ What can you see that differs from your observation of an unstained onion epidermis?

    _____

    ▫ Look among the cells until you find a dark, circular structure inside one of them. What is it?

    _____

    ▫ Frequently, darker spots can be seen within this dark structure. What are they? _____

- In Area A, make a drawing of one onion cell with a few adjoining cells to show how the cells fit together. Follow these instructions:
    - Draw the internal structures for the main cell only.
    - Label only the structures you see in your specimen.
    - Use the power you feel is best, but be sure to indicate which power you used to prepare your drawing.

Human Cheek Epithelial Cells

R E O

I. Prepare a wet mount of your cheek cells (or those of your lab partner) by following these instructions:

- Collect some mucous epithelial cells by rubbing the blunt end of a toothpick back and forth inside your cheek.
    - You should collect cells from only your own mouth.
    - To get the greatest concentration of cells, do not twirl the toothpick around, but use only one side.
- Remove the toothpick carefully, collecting as little saliva as possible.
- Put one drop of methylene blue stain on the center of a microscope slide.
- Immediately tap the edge of the toothpick with the cells several times in the stain.
- After this is done, carefully add the cover slip. Why do you need to be careful when you place the cover slip on top?

A

_____
_____
_____

II. View the cheek cells under low power.
- Look for isolated cells, not clumps.
- How can you tell the epithelial cells from the other debris that appears on the slide?

_____
_____

- These cells are called *mucous epithelial* cells. What does the word *mucous* tell us about the functions of these cells? (For help, use the index of your textbook.)

_____
_____
_____

R E O

III. Draw a single cheek epithelial cell in Area B.
- After you have found the cell you wish to draw, center it and then adjust your microscope to high power.
- Draw one epithelial cell and label all the parts you see.

B

Comparing Onion Epidermal and Cheek Epithelial Cells

I. What are some of the similarities between the onion epidermal cells and the cheek epithelial cells?

_____

_____

II. What are some of their differences?

_____

_____

III. Why aren't cheek cells all the same shape on the slide?

_____

_____

IV. If you stained both types of cells, which would stain more quickly and why?

_____

_____

V. What is the purpose of the plant cell wall?

_____

_____

VI. Animal cells do not have cell walls since animals have other means of physical support, such as the skeleton. What would be the problems if animal cells did have cell walls?

_____

_____

_____

_____

3b Cellular Organelles and Processes

Introduction

Anacharis is a common freshwater aquatic plant noted for its photosynthetic abilities. The edges of this plant's young leaves are thin enough to make possible microscopic viewing of living plant cells. You can see some colored organelles by observing these unstained living plant cells. Also, some cellular processes and reactions can be demonstrated. Other plant organelles not visible in anacharis can be seen in stained banana cells.

Materials

anacharis (or *Elodea*) leaves
concavity slides
dissection kit
cover slips
microscope
illuminator (optional)
salt solution
cotton swabs or toothpicks
glass slides
banana
iodine

Observing Anacharis (Elodea) Cells

R E O

I. Prepare a wet mount of an anacharis leaf by following these instructions:

• Use only young light-green leaves from the ends of the stem.

• Use a concavity slide (a slide with a concave depression in it). This type of slide will permit the thick leaf to be mounted and will allow the cover slip to lie flat. Use enough water to fill the concave portion of the slide.

• Be careful not to crush the leaf as you pick it up or mount it. (Often scissors and forceps help.)

II. Observe anacharis cells, using both the high power and the low power of the microscope.

• Be sure you are focused on cells on the margin (edge) of the leaf.

• The green chloroplasts make the clear, unstained nucleus difficult to see.

• By focusing at different depths in one cell, locate the large, clear area in the center of the cell (not the nucleus). What is this area called?

_____

• Observe the cytoplasmic streaming (carrying with it the chloroplasts) in the anacharis cells.

• If your specimen is not demonstrating any streaming, place the slide under an illuminator for two to five minutes. (Sometimes even this procedure does not help.)

• If your specimen does exhibit cytoplasmic streaming, tell the instructor so that others can observe yours.

• Why would cytoplasmic streaming be valuable for cells that have many chloroplasts?

_____

III. Make a drawing of two or three adjacent anacharis cells in Area A. Use the power you think best for drawing them and state which power you used.

IV. Preliminary work

- Situation: Anacharis is often used in aquariums as a decorative plant. You bought an anacharis plant for your saltwater aquarium. However, when you put it in your tank the plant shriveled and did not survive.
- Research question: How could the water in the tank have affected the plant?
- Hypothesis:

_____

V. Identify the variables and technique.

- How could you test your hypothesis?

_____

- What is the independent variable?

_____

- What is the dependent variable (what the scientist measures):

_____

- What is the control?

_____

VI. Prediction

- What results do you expect if the hypothesis is supported? Falsified?

_____

_____

VII. Test the hypothesis.

- Does the appearance of the cell support or falsify your hypothesis?

_____

_____

- From your results, explain why the plant in the saltwater aquarium wilted. (You may need to research in your text to explain the change.)

_____

_____

_____

- Is it possible to reverse the results? Explain.

_____

Observing Leucoplasts in Banana Cells

I. Answer the following questions before beginning:

- What are leucoplasts?

_____

- What is the major function of leucoplasts?

_____

- In what plant structures would you expect to find leucoplasts?

_____

II. Observe leucoplasts in banana cells.

- Using the broken end of a cotton swab (or a toothpick), make a smear wet mount of a small amount of mashed banana.

- Observe the slide on both the low power and the high power of your microscope. What do you see?

_____

- Stain the slide with an iodine stain. (NOTE: Iodine turns starch dark.)

  □ Use the same procedure for staining as was used to stain the onion epidermis in Lab 3a.

  □ Observe the slide. What do you see now?

_____

III. Prepare a drawing of a stained banana cell in Area B and label as many parts as you can.

A

B

name: _____

section: _____ date: _____

4 Photosynthesis

Introduction

Photosynthesis is a series of enzyme-catalyzed reactions that takes place in autotrophic organisms such as green plants. The plants use this process to convert energy from the sun to sugars they can use for cell growth. The leaves of the plant are the main photosynthetic factories. They contain chloroplasts with chlorophyll that absorbs the light energy. The overall formula shows the raw materials the plant needs to produce its food.

$$6H_2O + 6CO_2 + \text{light energy} \xrightarrow{\text{chlorophyll}} C_6H_{12}O_6 + 6O_2$$

In this lab you will use a technique that demonstrates the photosynthetic process in leaf disks. Leaf disks normally float in solution since they are filled with oxygen and carbon dioxide but will sink when infiltrated with a sodium bicarbonate solution. The sodium bicarbonate supplies the leaves with a source of carbon dioxide, a necessary precursor for photosynthesis. As seen in the equation, the leaves that undergo photosynthesis produce oxygen that is released into the leaf spaces, causing the leaf disks to float again. Respiration, which consumes oxygen, is also taking place in the leaves. The measurement of the leaf disks rising is an indirect way of quantifying the net rate of photosynthesis.

A Technique to Measure Photosynthesis

I. Setting up the experiment

- Remove the plunger from a 10 mL syringe.

- Use the hole punch or straw to cut 10–15 disks out of the leaf. Avoid punching out the leaf veins.

- Place the disks into the bottom of the syringe and replace the plunger as far as it will go without squashing the disks.

- Pull 5 mL of 0.2% sodium bicarbonate solution into the syringe. Tap the syringe to get the bubbles to rise and be released.

- Place your thumb over the syringe opening and pull back on the plunger to create a vacuum in the syringe. Maintain the vacuum for at least 10 seconds while shaking the disks to suspend them in the solution. Tiny air bubbles should be seen at the edge of the disks where the air is being pushed out of the leaf disk spaces. You can tap the syringe to release the air bubbles from the disks. The leaf disks should begin to sink.

- Release the vacuum. You may have to repeat this several times to get all of the leaf disks to sink.

- Pour the disks into a clear beaker or cup.

- Add 0.2% sodium bicarbonate solution to the cup to 2 cm. Separate the leaf disks so that they are not overlapping. Discard any disks that do not sink.

- Place the cup under a light source.

- Record the number of leaf disks at the surface after each minute for 15 minutes.

Goals

✓ Observe the results of photosynthesis in leaf disks

✓ Form and test a hypothesis about factors affecting photosynthesis

✓ Collect and analyze data from a photosynthesis experiment

Materials

10 mL oral syringe

hole punch or straw

leaves

0.2% sodium bicarbonate solution

plastic cups

ruler

desk lamps (or other illuminator, preferably with fluorescent bulb)

stop watch (or other timer)

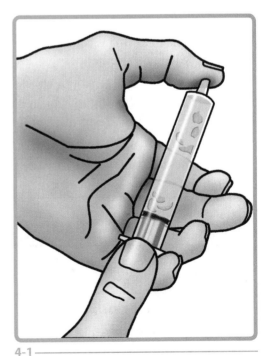

4-1

Technique required to sink leaf disks

II. Preliminary work: Factors affecting photosynthesis

- The green pigment, chlorophyll, is a light-absorbing molecule. Describe the role of chlorophyll in photosynthesis.

  _____

  _____

  _____

- What is the end product of light-dependent reactions involving chlorophyll?

  _____

  Predict the relationship between light intensity and this product.

  _____

- What role do enzymes play in the photosynthetic process?

  _____

  _____

  _____

- What factors affect the rate at which enzymes work?

  _____

  How would these factors affect the rate of photosynthesis?

  _____

  _____

  _____

Experiments to Determine Conditions for Photosynthesis

I. Devise an experiment to determine how varying factors affect the rate of photosynthesis using the leaf disk technique.

- The following is a list of possible conditions with which your class or group may wish to experiment, but you may try other possibilities.
  - □ Light intensity or wavelength
  - □ pH (Use vinegar and baking soda [sodium bicarbonate] to formulate solutions that have different pH values. Test papers will be needed to determine their pH.)
  - □ Temperature
- Research question:

  _____

- Hypothesis:

  _____

- What reason do you have for hypothesizing that your independent variable affects photosynthesis?

  _____

- Identify the variables in the experiment.
  - □ Independent variable:

    _____

- ▫ Dependent variable:

_____

- ▫ Standardized variables:

_____

_____

_____

_____

- ▫ Control group:

_____

_____

_____

- • Predict the results.
  - ▫ What results do you expect if the hypothesis is supported? Falsified?

_____

_____

_____

_____

_____

II. Run the experiment.
  - • Procedural technique (adapted to chosen independent variable)

_____

_____

_____

_____

_____

_____

_____

_____

_____

- • Record your data on the table on page 32 and create a line graph (on a separate sheet) with the time represented on the *x*-axis and the percent of leaf disks at the surface on the *y*-axis.

Number of Floating Leaf Disks				
Time (min)	Control group	Group 1	Group 2	Group 3
0				
1				
2				
3				
4				
5				
6				
7				
8				
9				
10				
11				
12				
13				
14				
15				
16				
17				
18				
19				
20				

Results for Photosynthesis

I. Further exploration

- The leaf is not only undergoing photosynthesis but also respiration. Write the equation for respiration.

   _____

   □ Describe the relationship between photosynthesis and respiration.

   _____

   _____

   _____

□ Predict what will happen if you place the control group in the dark after the leaf disks have risen to the top.

_____

_____

_____

_____

_____

_____

_____

- Test your prediction. Place the cup in the dark. Record the number, if any, of the leaf disks that are at the bottom after each minute for 15 minutes.

II. Answer the following questions:

- Based on your data, is photosynthesis affected by the factor you were testing? □ yes □ no
- Was your hypothesis supported or falsified? Use data to support your answer.

_____

_____

- At what range of the factor did photosynthesis happen at the fastest rate?

_____

_____

- At what range of the factor did photosynthesis happen at the slowest rate?

_____

_____

- What can you summarize regarding the rate of photosynthesis and the factor you were testing?

_____

_____

- If your results did not support your hypothesis, what factors may have affected your results?

_____

_____

- What steps would you recommend to improve the experiment you performed?

_____

_____

- Using the results from your experiment, explain how photosynthesis and respiration were demonstrated.

_____

_____

5a Mitosis and Meiosis

Introduction

Cell division is one of the basic biological processes. To understand thoroughly what happens during mitosis, however, you must understand what happens to the chromosomes in each of the phases.

After you master the process and significance of mitosis, you can understand meiosis (which forms gametes) and fertilization (which unites gametes). In order to grasp genetics and the concepts involved in the debate between biological evolutionism and creationism, you must understand the basic processes of mitosis and meiosis.

Goals

✓ Understand mitosis and learn its stages by drawing progressive diagrams

✓ Observe cells in various stages of mitosis

✓ Compare mitosis and meiosis

✓ Understand meiosis

🏠 A Description of Mitosis

R E O

To help your understanding of mitosis, use your text as a reference and fill in the following descriptions of the phases of animal mitosis before you begin your observations and drawings.

Mitosis is _____

_____

_____.

Materials

microscope

preserved slides of *Allium* root tips, l.s.

preserved slides of whitefish embryos prepared for viewing mitosis

I. Prophase
- In the cytoplasm
  - ▫ The divided centrosomes with their centrioles _____.
  - ▫ The centrosomes form the _____.
- Inside the nucleus
  - ▫ The chromosomes _____.
  - ▫ The chromosomes are composed of _____ that are attached at the _____.
  - ▫ The nucleolus _____.
  - ▫ The nuclear membrane _____.

II. Metaphase
- The centromeres of the chromosomes are located _____.
- The sister chromatids appear to _____.

III. Anaphase
- The sister chromatids _____.
- The spindle fibers _____.

IV. Telophase and cytokinesis
- Forming the nuclei
  - ▫ The daughter chromosomes _____.
  - ▫ At each pole of the cell _____.
  - ▫ The nuclear membrane _____.
  - ▫ The nucleoli _____.

- Outside the nucleus
  - ☐ The mitotic spindle _____.
  - ☐ The centrosomes _____.
- Cytokinesis
  - ☐ The plasma membrane _____.
  - ☐ The cytoplasm _____.

Mitosis in Plant Cells

In certain plant parts, almost all the cells carry on mitosis. If these areas are properly stained, chromosomes in the various phases of mitosis are easy to see.

I. Observe mitosis in a prepared root tip of *Allium* (onion).

- Obtain a preserved slide of an *Allium* root tip.
  - ☐ Notice the way the root tip has been sectioned (see Fig. 5a-1 and p. ix). Name and describe this type of sectioning.

  _____

  - ☐ Mitosis is carried on in an area just above the root cap, a protective group of cells located at the tip of the root. What is the name of this area? (Research in your text may be necessary.)

  _____

- Examine your slide under the microscope.
  - ☐ Using low power, locate the root cap and the area where mitosis is carried on.

(a)

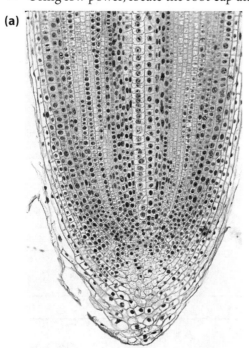

(b)

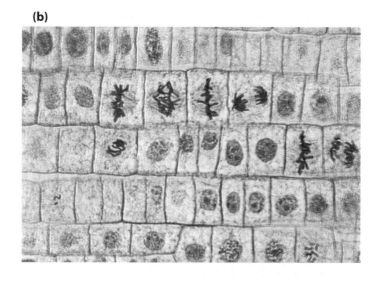

5a-1 ───

(a) Low-power microscope view showing onion root tip and (b) high-power view showing cells in various stages of mitosis

  - ☐ Using high power, observe various stages of mitosis.
    - ◆ Why do some of the root cells have no chromatin material? (Hint: How was the onion root cut to make this type of slide?)

  _____

♦ Find a cell in anaphase and count, as accurately as possible, how many chromosomes are found in an onion cell.

_____

♦ You will probably not see all the chromosomes. How many chromosomes are in an onion cell? (Research in your text.)

_____

♦ Account for the difference between the number you saw and the actual number.

_____

_____

_____

II. Draw a series of specimen drawings on page 38, showing mitosis in *Allium* root tips.

- Make sure you draw typical specimens of the various stages of mitosis. If the first one you find is not good, look for another.
- Draw one cell in each of the following phases in the spaces provided.
    1. Interphase
    2. Prophase
    3. Metaphase
    4. Anaphase
    5. Telophase
    6. Daughter cells
- Label any structures that you can identify.
- A timesaving tip: It is not necessary for you to draw the phases in order. If you find a good metaphase first, draw it in the metaphase space; then look for another phase. The drawings, however, must be in the proper boxes.
- Randomly pick twenty cells from the slide and assign each to one of the six stages. Are some phases more frequently seen than others?   ☐ yes   ☐ no
- Why do you think this is so?

_____

_____

_____

1.

Interphase

2.

Prophase

3.

Metaphase

4.

Anaphase

5.

Telophase

6.

Daughter cells

Mitosis in Animal Cells

In embryos mitosis happens rapidly. Thus a slide of an embryo, if properly prepared, will reveal phases of mitosis.

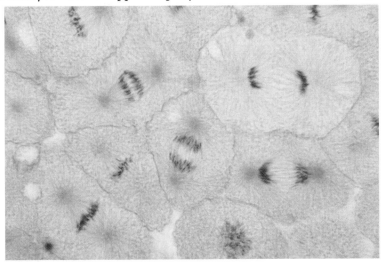

5a-2 ——————————————————

High-power microscope view showing whitefish embryo cells in various stages of mitosis

I. Observe animal mitosis in a whitefish embryo.

- Obtain a preserved slide of a whitefish embryo.

- Observe the slide on high power, looking for the various stages of mitosis. You should find all the phases. In the proper spaces, check the phases as you find them.

☐ Interphase

☐ Prophase

☐ Metaphase

☐ Anaphase

☐ Telophase

☐ Daughter cells

- How many chromosomes do you think a cell of a whitefish has? _____

  Based on your observations, can you be sure of this answer? ☐ yes ☐ no

- Explain why you can or cannot be sure.

  _____

  _____

II. Draw a series of specimen drawings on page 40, showing mitosis in whitefish embryos.

- Make sure you draw typical specimens of the various stages of mitosis.

- Draw one cell in each of the following phases in the spaces provided and label any structures you can identify.

  1. Interphase
  2. Prophase
  3. Metaphase
  4. Anaphase
  5. Telophase
  6. Daughter cells

1.

Interphase

2.

Prophase

3.

Metaphase

4.

Anaphase

5.

Telophase

6.

Daughter cells

III. Compare mitosis in animals and plants. List several differences between mitosis in plants and in animals by filling in the spaces below.

- In plants _____,
  while in animals _____.
- In plants _____,
  while in animals _____.
- In plants _____,
  while in animals _____.

A Description of Meiosis

To help your understanding of meiosis, use your text as a reference and fill in the following descriptions of the phases of meiosis in animals.

I. First division

- Prophase
  - Before going through meiosis, the mother cell must have the _____-ploid chromosome number.
  - The duplicated homologous chromosomes _____ to form a _____.
- Metaphase
  - The tetrads _____.
- Anaphase
  - The sister chromatids _____.
  - The homologous pairs of chromosomes _____.
- Telophase and cytokinesis
  - The chromosomes _____.
  - The cytoplasm _____.
  - The result of the first division of meiosis is two _____-ploid cells, each containing _____ of each homologous pair of chromosomes found in the mother cell.

II. Second division

- Prophase
  - Since the chromosomes do not uncoil after the first division of meiosis, the cells are ready to undergo the rest of the phases of meiosis almost immediately following the first division.
- Metaphase
  - The chromosomes in each cell _____.
- Anaphase
  - The sister chromatids in each cell _____.
  - The resulting daughter chromosomes _____.
- Telophase and cytokinesis
  - The nuclei are _____.
  - The cytoplasm in each cell _____.
  - At the end of the second division of meiosis, there are _____ cells, each of which contains the _____-ploid number of chromosomes. These cells are called the _____.

Comparison of Mitosis and Meiosis

Mitosis is the asexual reproduction of cells. Meiosis is the formation of gametes in preparation for sexual reproduction. The processes, while similar, have noticeable differences.

I. Compare the phases.

- Compare mitosis and meiosis by filling in the chart below. All the information you need is in your text (see especially the diagrams on pp. 106–7 and 110); however, some of the answers will require thought.

- A note about completing the last column: If the stage has sister chromatids, check the number of sister chromatids (not individual chromosomes). If the stage has daughter chromosomes, check the total number of daughter chromosomes.

A Comparison of Mitosis and Meiosis

Type and phase	Stage has sister chromatids or daughter chromosomes	Chromosomes or chromatids moving toward, at, or moving away from the equatorial plane	Number of chromosomes or chromatids in each cell (2n = 6)	
Mitosis prophase	☐ sister ☐ daughter	☐ moving toward ☐ at equatorial plane ☐ moving away	☐ 3 ☐ 6	☐ 9 ☐ 12
Meiosis prophase (1st division)	☐ sister ☐ daughter	☐ moving toward ☐ at equatorial plane ☐ moving away	☐ 3 ☐ 6	☐ 9 ☐ 12
Mitosis metaphase	☐ sister ☐ daughter	☐ moving toward ☐ at equatorial plane ☐ moving away	☐ 3 ☐ 6	☐ 9 ☐ 12
Meiosis metaphase (2nd division)	☐ sister ☐ daughter	☐ moving toward ☐ at equatorial plane ☐ moving away	☐ 3 ☐ 6	☐ 9 ☐ 12
Mitosis anaphase	☐ sister ☐ daughter	☐ moving toward ☐ at equatorial plane ☐ moving away	☐ 3 ☐ 6	☐ 9 ☐ 12
Meiosis anaphase (1st division)	☐ sister ☐ daughter	☐ moving toward ☐ at equatorial plane ☐ moving away	☐ 3 ☐ 6	☐ 9 ☐ 12
Mitosis telophase	☐ sister ☐ daughter	no directional movement	☐ 3 ☐ 6	☐ 9 ☐ 12
Meiosis telophase (2nd division)	☐ sister ☐ daughter	no directional movement	☐ 3 ☐ 6	☐ 9 ☐ 12

name: _____

II. Answer the following questions comparing mitosis and meiosis.

- In metaphase, what is the name of the chromatin material that lines up on the equatorial plane in
    □ mitosis?

    _____

    □ meiosis, first division?

    _____

    □ meiosis, second division?

    _____

- In anaphase, what is the name of the chromatin material that is moving toward opposite poles in
    □ mitosis?

    _____

    □ meiosis, first division?

    _____

    □ meiosis, second division?

    _____

5b Genetics

Introduction

It is easy to watch someone else work on a solution to a problem. Often, however, it is quite another thing to take a similar problem and work it out yourself. Only when you thoroughly understand the process can you work a problem "from scratch." If you can work the series of problems in this laboratory exercise outside of class, you probably understand the simple genetics presented in BIOLOGY. If you cannot solve them, you need more study and instruction. If you have difficulty with these problems, seek help from your teacher.

Goals
✓ Work lab problems to increase understanding of genetics
✓ Measure knowledge and understanding of basic genetic principles

Materials
none

Part I Monohybrid Problems with Simple Dominance

Determining Genotypes from Phenotypes

In humans, the ability to taste the chemical phenylthiocarbamide (PTC) is an inherited, dominant characteristic. For these exercises use the symbol *T* to represent the dominant allele and *t* to represent the recessive allele.

I. The genotype for a person who cannot taste PTC would be written _____.

II. The genotype for a person who can taste PTC would be written as either _____ or

_____.

III. In the answer above, put a star (*) by the genotype for a person who is heterozygous.

• Is there any difference between the phenotypes of these two people who can taste PTC? ☐ yes ☐ no

• Explain. _____

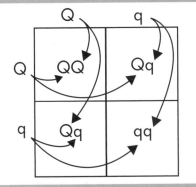

How to Fill In a Punnett Square

• Female gametes are written across the top of a Punnett square; male gametes are written along the left side.

• The symbols used on the top and side of the Punnett square represent possible gametes, not genotypes for individuals.

• The symbols you write inside the Punnett square are possible gamete combinations, or the possible genotypes of the offspring.

Using Punnett Squares

I. Using the Punnett square on the right, cross a homozygous male taster with a female nontaster.

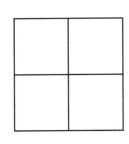

• In this Punnett square, is it possible to have the following offspring?

    A. A heterozygous taster? ☐ yes ☐ no

    B. A heterozygous nontaster? ☐ yes ☐ no

    C. A homozygous taster? ☐ yes ☐ no

    D. A homozygous nontaster? ☐ yes ☐ no

• Place a star next to the genotype/phenotype combination above that is impossible.

II. One of the offspring of the previous cross marries a person who is known to be heterozygous.

- Is there any possibility of there being a nontaster in the next generation? ☐ yes ☐ no
- To prove your answer, diagram the cross on the Punnett square to the right and circle the genotype of the nontaster (if there is one).
- What is the phenotypic ratio of this cross? (Give the numbers and the description of what the numbers stand for.)

_____

- What is the genotypic ratio of this cross? (Give the numbers and the description of what the numbers stand for.)

_____

Suggestions for Solving Genetics Problems

1. Determine as many genotypes as you can.
   - Since a person who has the recessive phenotype must have the recessive genotype, you know the genotype of that person.
   - Since a person who has the dominant phenotype must have at least one dominant allele, note that as part of that person's genotype.
2. Determine whether the person's parents or offspring tell you anything about the person's genotype.
   - If the parents are known to be purebred (homozygous) for a trait, that may give you some information regarding the individual's genotype.
   - If the offspring are known to be purebred (homozygous) for a trait, that may also give you information regarding the individual's genotype.
3. Put the information you have on a Punnett square.
4. Determine what you can, based on the information you have.

III. Mr. Johnson cannot taste PTC, but his wife can. Mrs. Johnson's mother cannot taste PTC, but her father can.

- Is it possible for the Johnsons to have a child that can taste PTC? ☐ yes ☐ no
- Is it possible for the Johnsons to have a child that cannot taste PTC? ☐ yes ☐ no
- Demonstrate your answers on the Punnett square to the right.
- Explain how you can know Mrs. Johnson's genotype.

_____
_____
_____

5b Genetics
Part II Problems with Pedigree Charts

Examine the Pedigree Chart below. It shows several generations of tasters and nontasters of PTC. Some of the genotypes are supplied. As you work out the problems below, you may need to fill in the genotypes of individuals on the Pedigree Chart.

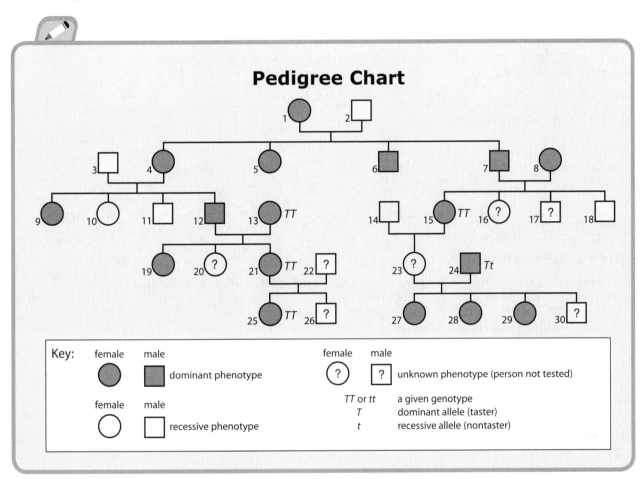

Pedigree Chart

Key:
female	male

dominant phenotype

female — ? / male — ? unknown phenotype (person not tested)

female — male recessive phenotype

TT or *tt* a given genotype
T dominant allele (taster)
t recessive allele (nontaster)

Be sure you have read the material about pedigrees in your text (pp. 116–17).

I. Answer the following questions regarding the pedigree of tasters and nontasters.

- What is the phenotype of individual 1? _____
- Write all the possible genotypes of individual 1. _____
- What is the phenotype of individual 2? _____
- Write all the possible genotypes of individual 2. _____
- Diagram the possible crosses between individuals 1 and 2 on the Punnett squares to the right.
- Note carefully the phenotypes of the offspring of individuals 1 and 2 as given on the pedigree. Give the genotypes for the following individuals:
  4 _____ 5 _____ 6 _____ 7 _____
- Would it be possible for any of their future brothers or sisters to exhibit the recessive trait?
  ☐ yes ☐ no

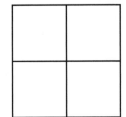

R
E
O

Explain your answer.

_____

_____

- Enter the genotypes for individuals 1, 2, 4, 5, 6, and 7 on the pedigree. Be sure to indicate those alleles you are not sure of by a dash (example: "*T* –" or "– –").

II. What is the expected phenotypic ratio for the crossing of individuals 3 and 4?

- Fill in the cross on the Punnett square to the right.

- Record the phenotypic ratio from the Punnett square, being sure to tell what the numbers stand for.

_____

III. What is the genotype of individual 12? _____

IV. Individual 20 died in infancy.

- Is it possible to tell the child's phenotype? ☐ yes ☐ no   If so, what is it? _____
- Is it possible to tell the child's genotype? ☐ yes ☐ no   If so, what is it? _____

V. From the information given on the pedigree, is it possible to determine the phenotype of individual 22?

☐ yes ☐ no   If so, what is it? _____

- Is it possible to tell the genotype of his son (individual 26)? ☐ yes ☐ no   If so, what is it? _____

VI. From information given on the pedigree, is it possible to tell the genotype of individual 8?

☐ yes ☐ no   If so, what is it? _____

- Explain how you know or do not know.

_____

_____

VII. Is it possible to know the phenotype

- of individual 16? ☐ yes ☐ no
- of individual 17? ☐ yes ☐ no
- If so, what are they? 16 _____ 17 _____
- Explain how you know or do not know.

_____

_____

VIII. What must be the phenotype and genotype of individual 23? _____

IX. Is it possible that individual 30 expresses the recessive trait? ☐ yes ☐ no

Is it possible that he expresses the dominant trait? ☐ yes ☐ no

- Which is more likely? _____
- Explain your choice.

_____

_____

_____

5b Genetics

Part III Problems with Incomplete Dominance

Read carefully the information about incomplete dominance in your text (pp. 117–18). Incomplete dominance problems can be worked easily on Punnett squares.

R **E** **O** Simple Incomplete Dominance Problems

When a homozygous red radish plant is crossed with a homozygous white radish plant, purple radishes result.

I. Determine the alleles in radishes.

- In incomplete dominance, both alleles are usually expressed with the same uppercase (capital) letter. We will use C for this cross.

- The possible traits are shown with lowercase superscripts.

  - Give the genotype of a white radish. _____

  - Give the genotype of a red radish. _____

  - Give the genotype of a purple radish. _____

- Determine the possible gametes of

  - a white radish _____

  - a red radish _____

  - a purple radish _____

II. Complete these radish crosses.

- If the pollen from a white radish fertilizes the egg of a red radish, what will be the genotypes and the phenotypes of the offspring? Prove your answer on the Punnett square to the right.

  _____

- If pollen from a red radish flower fertilizes the egg of another flower on the same plant, what will be the genotypes and phenotypes of the offspring? Why?

  _____

  _____

- If two purple radishes are cross-pollinated, what are the genotypic and phenotypic ratios of the F_1 generation? Prove your answer by making the proper cross on the Punnett square to the right.

  Genotypic:

  _____

  Phenotypic:

  _____

- If a red radish and a purple radish are cross-pollinated, what will be the phenotypic and genotypic ratios? Complete a Punnett square of the cross on your own paper if needed.

  Genotypic:

  _____

  Phenotypic:

  _____

- Will the ratios given in the preceding question be the same if a white radish and a purple radish are crossed? Explain.

_____

A Challenging Incomplete Dominance Problem

This problem is more complex, but if you understand the material already discussed, you can figure it out.

The litter resulting from the mating of two short-tailed cats contains three kittens without tails, two with long tails, and six with short tails.

I. Diagram a cross that will show the above results on the Punnett square to the right. First, however, you will need to give a key for the letters you choose to represent the alleles.

Key:

_____

_____

_____

_____

II. What are the genotypes of the parents? ☐ homozygous ☐ heterozygous ☐ one of each

III. Does the ratio of the kittens given in the statement agree with the ratio obtained from the Punnett square? Is it close enough for you to be sure you used the proper genotypes when you diagrammed the cross?

_____

_____

Another Challenging Incomplete Dominance Problem

The fur of some types of mice illustrates incomplete dominance. The fur can be "black agouti," "normal black," or "albino" (white). A mouse that is heterozygous is "normal black." Use *b* to indicate the allele for black agouti fur and *w* to indicate the allele for albino white fur.

I. Determine the possible genotypes in mice.
- Give the genotype of a black agouti mouse. _____
- Give the genotype of a normal black mouse. _____
- Give the genotype of an albino mouse. _____

II. In the Punnett square to the right, diagram a cross between a normal black mouse and an albino mouse. What are the genotypic and phenotypic ratios in the F_1 generation?
- Genotypic: _____
- Phenotypic: _____

III. This cross produces a litter of 15 mice. Eight of the mice are normal black, and seven are albino. Was the expected phenotypic ratio obtained? Explain.

_____

_____

_____

5b Genetics

section: _____ date: _____

Part IV Problems with Multiple Alleles

Occasionally there will be more than one pair of alleles possible at a single locus. Three or more alleles, rather than just one set of contrasting traits, may be possible. Read carefully the material in your text regarding multiple alleles (pp. 119–20).

Inheritance of the ABO Blood Types

The human blood types—A, B, AB, and O—are determined by multiple alleles, two dominant and one recessive. They are often written

Dominant: I^A, I^B Recessive: i

In this example the I represents the chromosome, and the superscripts A and B the dominant alleles. The i represents the recessive allele on a chromosome.

I. Using the above symbols, indicate all the possible genotypes for the phenotypes given below. (NOTE: Two blood types have two possible genotypes; the other two have only one.)

- Blood type A _____
- Blood type AB _____
- Blood type B _____
- Blood type O _____

II. A man who is heterozygous for blood type A marries a woman who is heterozygous for blood type B.

- Write their genotypes below.
  - Man _____
  - Woman _____
- Could a child with blood type O be born into this family? ☐ yes ☐ no

  Prove your answer on the Punnett square to the right.
- Could a child with blood type A be born into this family? ☐ yes ☐ no
- Could a child with blood type B be born into this family? ☐ yes ☐ no
- Could a child with blood type AB be born into this family? ☐ yes ☐ no

Additional Multiple Allele Problems

I. Is it possible for a woman with blood type O to have a child with blood type AB? ☐ yes ☐ no

Explain your answer. (You may need to use a Punnett square to demonstrate the cross.)

_____

_____

_____

_____

II. Is it possible for a man with blood type AB to have a child with type O blood? ☐ yes ☐ no

Explain your answer. (You may need to use a Punnett square to demonstrate the cross.)

_____

_____

_____

_____

III. Is it possible for a woman with type A blood to have a child with type O blood? ☐ yes ☐ no

Explain your answer. (You may need to use a Punnett square to demonstrate the proper cross.)

_____

_____

_____

_____

IV. A woman with blood type O marries a man with blood type B. Their first child has type B blood, and their second child has type O blood.

- Is it possible for the man's genotype to be $I^B I^B$? ☐ yes ☐ no
- Diagram this cross on the Punnett square to the right.
- Is it possible for this couple's future children to have a different blood type than either parent? ☐ yes ☐ no

5b Genetics

Part V Problems with Dihybrid Crosses

A dihybrid cross deals with two sets of characteristics at the same time. Read carefully the material on dihybrid crosses in your text (pp. 120–21).

The abilities of some people to taste PTC and roll their tongue into a U shape when it is extended from the mouth are dominant characteristics. We will call those who exhibit the dominant traits "tasters" and "rollers," and we will call those who exhibit the recessive traits "nontasters" and "nonrollers." The capital letters *T* and *R* will be used for the dominant alleles, and the lowercase letters *t* and *r* for the recessive alleles in this exercise.

A Simple Dihybrid Cross

R E O

I. A man who is homozygous for tongue rolling and homozygous for the ability to taste PTC (genotype *RRTT*) marries a woman who is homozygous for both recessive traits.

- Write the genotype for his wife.

  _____

- What possible gametes can the husband form? (Remember that a gamete will have one of every homologous pair of chromosomes. It is thus impossible to have an *RR* gamete or a *TT* gamete.)

  _____

- What possible gametes can the wife form?

  _____

- On the Punnett square on the right, cross these two people. What is the genotype of their offspring? (NOTE: You should have only one genotype for the offspring, and that genotype must have four letters. If yours does not work this way, go back and check your work.)

  _____

roller (*RR* or *Rr*)   **nonroller (*rr*)**

5b-1 ——————————————————————
Tongues of a roller and a nonroller

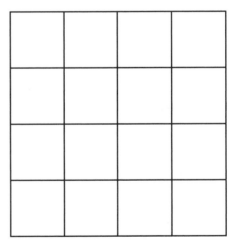

II. A man who is heterozygous for both rolling his tongue and tasting PTC marries a woman with the same genotype.

- Write the genotypes for them:

  man _____   woman _____

- What are the possible gametes they can form?

  man _____   woman _____

- Cross this couple on the Punnett square to the right.

- Give the resulting phenotypic ratio in the proper spaces.

  _____ roller-taster(s)

  _____ roller-nontaster(s)

  _____ nonroller-taster(s)

  _____ nonroller-nontaster(s)

<table>
<tr><td></td><td></td><td></td><td></td></tr>
<tr><td></td><td></td><td></td><td></td></tr>
<tr><td></td><td></td><td></td><td></td></tr>
<tr><td></td><td></td><td></td><td></td></tr>
</table>

Another Dihybrid Cross

In fruit flies, vestigial wings and hairy bodies are recessive traits that are caused by recessive alleles located on different chromosomes. The normal alleles (long wings and hairless body) are dominant.

I. Using the above information, fill in the following blanks with symbols for the alleles.

  _____ is the allele for vestigial wings.

  _____ is the allele for long wings.

  _____ is the allele for hairless bodies.

  _____ is the allele for hairy bodies.

II. Suppose a vestigial-winged, hairy-bodied male is crossed with a homozygous dominant female. (Work the Punnett squares for these questions on a separate sheet of paper.)

- What offspring would be expected? Show genotypes and phenotypes as ratios.

  □ Genotype:

  _____

  □ Phenotype:

  _____

- If these F_1 offspring are permitted to mate freely, what would you expect their offspring (the F_2) to be like? Show genotypes and phenotypes as ratios.

  □ Genotype:

  _____

  _____

  □ Phenotype:

  _____

  _____

Laboratory Exercise 5b

name: _____

5b Genetics

section: _____ date: _____

Part VI Problems with Sex-linked Traits

Carefully study the pedigree of Queen Victoria and Prince Albert on page 125 of your text, and read the material regarding sex-linked traits on pages 123–26. Hemophilia, a recessive trait controlled by a gene found on the X chromosome, is sometimes called "bleeder's disease." Traits on the X chromosome that are not found on the Y chromosome are usually written as superscripts (above and to the right) of the symbol for the chromosome—the X. The Y, which lacks the gene for this trait, is left without a superscript. Since hemophilia is recessive, we will use the letter h for the hemophilia gene and H for the normal, dominant gene.

R E O

I. Write the genotypes for the people described below. One phenotype given below is impossible and does not have a genotype. Put a star in the blank for the impossible phenotype.

- A normal female who carries the gene for hemophilia: _____
- A normal male who carries the gene for hemophilia: _____
- A normal female without a gene for hemophilia: _____
- A normal male without a gene for hemophilia: _____
- A hemophiliac female: _____
- A hemophiliac male: _____

R E O

II. Answer the following.

- What is Queen Victoria's genotype? _____
- What is Prince Albert's genotype? _____
- Cross Queen Victoria and Prince Albert on Punnett Square A.
    - In the proper boxes of the Punnett square, write the names of their offspring.
    - Is it possible to have a noncarrier female from Victoria and Albert? ☐ yes ☐ no

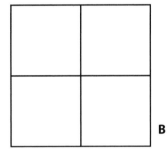

A

- On Punnett Square B, cross Beatrice of the first generation with Henry of Battenburg.
    - Show how they were able to have Alexander and Maurice, both males, but one with hemophilia and the other without the disease. (Write their names in the proper spaces of the Punnett square.)
    - Is it possible to have a hemophiliac female from this cross? ☐ yes ☐ no

B

- On Punnett Square C, cross Alice of the first generation and Louis IV.
    - To show how they can have Elizabeth and Irene, both females, but one a carrier and the other a noncarrier, write their names in the proper spaces of the Punnett square.
    - Is it possible to have a hemophiliac female from this cross? ☐ yes ☐ no

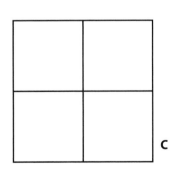

C

- If Frederick William married his cousin Alice (both of the second generation), could they produce a hemophiliac female? ☐ yes ☐ no
    - Prove your answer on Punnett Square D. If there is a hemophiliac female, circle her genotype.

D

- Since there is no difference between the phenotype of a female carrier and the phenotype of a normal female, how have the people who compiled this chart been able to determine who were carriers and who were not?

  _____

- The current British ruling family (Queen Elizabeth II, fourth generation) has gone for six generations without a hemophiliac individual. This is because Edward VII, Victoria's son, did not have hemophilia. Explain how this fact eliminated the hemophilia gene from the current line of English rulers.

  _____

  _____

  _____

- Imagine that Viscount Trematon (third generation) married a woman who was a carrier for hemophilia.
  - Diagram this cross on Punnett Square E.
  - What percentage of the females and what percentage of the males from this cross would be expected to have hemophilia?

    _____

- What are the possible genotypes for the daughters of Tsar Nicholas II and Alix (second generation)? (You may want to demonstrate your answer with a Punnett square.) Why are there question marks in these circles?

  _____

  _____

E

6 Genetic Research

Introduction

Genetic research makes headlines today more frequently than ever before. Scientists are not yet ready to announce a cure for all kinds of cancer or a way to replace a worn-out heart or liver with a cloned (genetically identical) one. Nor have they engineered a plant that will withstand heat, frost, drought, and flood and still produce abundant, edible, nutritious fruit. But many of the experiments being done today yield information that brings those and other genetic dreams closer to reality.

With all abilities come not only opportunities but also responsibilities. For example, when you begin to drive a car, you have not only the opportunity to drive the car for good purposes (going to school or church, doing errands for the family) but also the opportunity to improperly use the car (going places you should not go, driving recklessly). It is your responsibility to use the car as it should be used.

The same principle holds true for scientific information. Most people would rejoice at the announcement that scientists had learned to use a few blood cells to grow kidneys that can be implanted when needed and will not be rejected. Such information, however, could also permit people to do things that might not meet with such universal approval and might even violate scriptural principles of morality.

In this exercise you will be asked to read about a current area of genetic research or application of genetic knowledge and to speculate about the good and the bad that could result from the information's being learned and used.

> ### Goals
> ✓ Learn about the current topics of genetic research
> ✓ Make some decisions regarding genetic research

> ### Materials
> library or Internet access

Research

I. In a periodical that has come out within the past two years, find an article that deals with current genetic research or application.

- The article may deal with any of the following:
  □ Genetic screening
  □ Artificial reproduction (artificial insemination, test-tube fertilization, surrogate motherhood)
  □ Cloning
  □ Genetic engineering
  □ Stem cell research
  □ Gene therapy
  □ DNA fingerprinting
  □ Genetically modified organisms or crops

- The article may deal with humans, plants, animals, protists, fungi, bacteria, or the release of genetically altered organisms into the environment.

II. If possible, find other articles dealing with the same genetic research or application of knowledge.

- Look in other periodicals that came out about the same time.

- Use the Internet to search for additional information or recent developments.

- Look for reactions of scientists, physicians, scientific groups, activist groups, political leaders, government agencies, and other groups regarding this or closely related research or applications.

Analysis

In some of the following spaces you may need to indicate "none." In those answers where you deal with scriptural matters, be sure to give references to support your statements. Answer the questions in sections II–V on your own paper.

I. Describe the genetic research or application.

- Who or what group did the research or experimentation?

  _____

- What organisms are currently involved in this genetic research or application?

  _____

- What part of the organism(s) is currently involved?

  _____

- What has been done? (Summarize the process of doing it, not the results.)

  _____

  _____

  _____

  _____

- What results have been achieved?

  _____

  _____

  _____

  _____

II. What are the projected outcomes of this genetic research or application?

- What is projected as the immediate outcome (benefits) of this genetic research or application? Mention any time frame that is given.

- What are the projected long-range benefits of this genetic research or application? Mention any time frame that is given.

- What drawbacks or potential problems connected with this genetic research or application are mentioned?

III. What is your analysis of the present research and its present application?

- Were any scriptural principles violated in the discovery of the information (research)? If so, explain.

- Is the present application(s) of the information in violation of scriptural principles? If so, explain.

- What advantages or drawbacks not mentioned above might emerge regarding the present use of the information?

IV. What is your analysis of the future uses of this genetic research or application?

- To what future studies might this information contribute?

- What potential scriptural problems might arise from the use of this information?

- What advantages or drawbacks not mentioned above might arise regarding the future use of the information?

V. What can you recommend to prevent present and future abuse of this knowledge and unacceptable applications of the knowledge?

7a DNA Extraction

Introduction

DNA can be found in most cell types in your body. Although the amount in a single cell is microscopic, it is a simple process to collect a quantity that is visible without magnification. In an earlier lab, stains were used to visualize the DNA within the cell. In this lab, you will painlessly remove cells from your own mouth and, through simple chemical and physical reactions, release the DNA from the nuclei of those cells. Once you separate it from the other cellular contents, the DNA will be visible to you.

The extraction and analysis of DNA in professional labs requires the use of enzymes and is conducted under very controlled conditions. After extraction, the DNA molecules are analyzed by several different techniques. For example, the DNA strands can be cut with enzymes and then separated through a process called gel electrophoresis. The end result is an image of light and dark bands that is unique to each organism; this image is called a DNA fingerprint. The process of DNA fingerprinting will be modeled in the next lab exercise.

Goals

✓ Perform a simple DNA extraction using mucous epithelial cells

✓ Observe DNA strands separated from the nucleus

Materials

distilled water

graduated cylinder

2 small clear plastic cups

6% salt solution

25% solution of clear liquid dish soap

rubbing (isopropyl or ethyl) alcohol or denatured alcohol, ice cold

glass or wooden stirring rod

2 test tubes

phenol red indicator

Procedure

I. Set up your experiment.

- You are going to isolate DNA from your own cells after collecting them in a cup of water. If this sample were going to be used for DNA fingerprinting, the sample would have to be from only one person—no contaminating DNA from any other source. In this experiment, contaminating DNA could potentially be introduced from the water used to collect the DNA sample.

- Research question: Is there contaminating DNA in the water used to collect the sample?

- Hypothesis:

  _____

  _____

- Identify the variables:
  - Independent variable: _____
  - Dependent variable: _____
  - Standardized variables:

    _____

    _____

    _____

    _____

       □ Which cup represents the control group, and which represents the experimental group?

_____

_____

- Predict the results:
  - □ What results do you expect if your hypothesis is supported?

  _____

  _____

  - □ What results do you expect if your hypothesis is falsified?

  _____

  _____

- Now you can set up and run the experiment.

II. Collect your cheek cells.
- Using a graduated cylinder, measure 15 mL of distilled water and pour it into a plastic cup.
- Swirl this water around in your mouth for at least thirty seconds. The more vigorously you swirl, the more cheek cells you will collect.
- Spit this swirled water back into the cup. Label the cup with cheek cells *Cup 1.*
- What type of cells have you just collected? (Hint: See Lab 3a.)

_____

- Observe and describe the appearance of your solution:

_____

- Measure another 15 mL of distilled water, and pour it into a second cup. Label this cup with plain water *Cup 2.*
- Observe and describe the appearance of your solution:

_____

III. Add the solutions to the cups.
- Using a graduated cylinder, add 5 mL of the salt solution to the contents of each cup.
- Using the same graduated cylinder, add 5 mL of the soap solution to the contents of each cup.
- Why is soap used to release DNA? (Hint: Soap cleans dishes because it breaks fats apart.)

_____

_____

- Swirl the cups around to mix the salt and soap solutions with the other contents of the cup.
- Observe and describe the appearance of the solutions in each cup at this point.
  - □ Cup 1:

  _____

  - □ Cup 2:

  _____

IV. Separate the DNA from the solution.
- Use a graduated cylinder to measure out 15 mL of the ice cold alcohol.

- After tilting Cup 1, **SLOWLY** pour the alcohol down the side so that it forms a separate layer on top of the solution already in the cup. It is important to do this slowly. If you allow mixing to occur, your results will be affected since you will most likely not be able to isolate the DNA.

- Gently put the cup down without mixing the layers.

- Repeat this process with Cup 2.

- Allow the cups to sit for two to three minutes.

- The ice cold alcohol and the salt solution make it impossible for the DNA to stay in solution. Hold the cup up to the light and look at the layer just below the alcohol.

- Observe and describe the appearance of the solutions just below the alcohol layer in each cup at this point.

  □ Cup 1:

  _____

  □ Cup 2:

  _____

- If you see bubbles rising up through the alcohol, observe them carefully. They may be drawing white "strings" of thousands of DNA molecules along with them as they rise.

- Why does the DNA material collect between the water and the alcohol?

  _____

  _____

  _____

V. Physically remove a DNA sample from the cup if it is present.

- Insert a glass or wooden stirring rod into the cup, putting it the whole way down so that it touches the bottom of the cup.

- Slowly turn it in one direction, but *do not stir*.

- Look for the white strings to be collecting around the rod as you turn it.

- Gently remove the rod. There should be clumps containing many DNA molecules wound around the rod.

- Repeat these steps with Cup 2.

VI. Verify the presence of DNA.

- Insert the rod containing the DNA strings into a test tube containing 15 mL of the 6% salt solution.

- Spin the rod to dislodge the DNA into the water.

- What happens to your DNA molecules when you place them in the water?

  _____

- Add five drops of phenol red indicator to the solution. (Be careful with the indicator as it may permanently stain clothing.)

- Phenol red indicator ranges in color from yellow at a pH of 6.8 to red at 8.2.

- What color change, if any, did you observe when phenol red was added to your water and cell solution?

  _____

- What does this tell you about your solution and the type of materials it contains?

  _____

- Extraction is defined as removing a substance using chemical and/or physical means.

  □ What chemical means did you use to extract your DNA?

  _____

◻ What physical means did you use?

_____

🏠 *Analysis*

VII. Analyze your results.

- Do the data support your hypothesis? Explain using specific results.

_____

_____

_____

- Answer the research question in terms of whether the DNA sample could be used for a DNA fingerprint.

_____

_____

_____

- Assume that you performed this experiment, but you found no DNA in either cup. What are several factors that might account for these results?

_____

_____

_____

_____

_____

_____

- Why was it necessary to use the same water source for both cups?

_____

_____

_____

_____

- What problems can result from running an experiment without the proper controls?

_____

_____

_____

_____

7b DNA Analysis

Introduction

DNA fingerprinting has become an accepted technique when analyzing evidence in criminal investigations, paternity cases, and victim identification in the case of disasters. The technique is based on the fact that each individual has a unique DNA sequence. There are several DNA sequences that are the same in people and even animals since we use similar processes such as cellular respiration. However, everyone has variable DNA sequences in noncoding regions that differ, resulting in individual DNA fingerprints. The more these regions are probed, the more specific the DNA fingerprint is.

DNA fingerprinting involves a series of techniques that result in a pattern of DNA that looks similar to a bar code, which can be used for DNA analysis. The first step requires isolation and purification of a DNA sample, similar to the technique you learned in Lab 7a. However, DNA that is isolated is useless until it is analyzed in some way. In this lab, you are going to simulate the steps of DNA fingerprinting to analyze the "DNA sample." A crime has occurred and you must identify the culprit!

> ### Goals
> ✓ Examine crime scene evidence
> ✓ Model the process of DNA fingerprinting

> ### Materials
> none

The Crime

The sophomore class had developed a flawless recipe for Super Chocolate Brownies. They were entering the recipe along with samples to the school brownie competition. The competition was the final event in the school's spirit week, and this year it was the tie-breaking event! But when one of the sophomores walked to her classroom after lunch, she was shocked to see crime scene tape covering the door. When she looked into the room, she saw investigators huddled around the brownie pan, and the recipe had vanished! Who could have done such a thing?

The Evidence

The following crime scene report was turned in by the investigative team.

Basic Information

Illegal action: Theft
Complaint status: Pending DNA results
Property involved: Super Chocolate Brownies and recipe
Value: Spirit week trophy . . . Incalculable

Crime Scene Data

The brownies had been placed on Mrs. B.'s desk, the classroom teacher, to cool during lunch to be taken to the competition later in the day. Mrs. B. reported the crime after she returned to the classroom and found the recipe missing . . . and the brownies eaten. There was no forced entry into the classroom from outside the building, and the classroom door had been left open. The investigative team dusted for fingerprints but the room was wiped clean. Mr. Steel, the school custodian, was questioned and claimed to have cleaned the classroom during lunch. He had observed several students come by the classroom during lunch. The classroom was combed for evidence by the forensics unit. A team jacket with hairs attached to the collar was found near the desk. The forensics technician said a saliva sample could be taken from the half-eaten brownies that were left behind.

Suspect Data

The microscopic examination of the hairs, the presence of the coat, and visual observation of the classroom led to circumstantial evidence pointing to 4 suspects that could have been involved in the crime.

Suspect 1:

Name: Stan Steel

Occupation: custodian

Circumstantial evidence: Stan was in charge of cleaning the classrooms. He had access to the brownies.

Suspect 2:

Name: Chip Lee

Occupation: student

Circumstantial evidence: Chip was seen entering the classroom by Mr. Steel. He is known for his love of brownies (especially those with chocolate chips!).

Suspect 3:

Name: Brock Lee

Occupation: student

Circumstantial evidence: Brock is Chip's twin brother and plans to open a chocolate shop after graduating. He would love to get his hands on the Super Chocolate Brownie recipe.

Suspect 4:

Name: Jim Sox

Occupation: team captain of senior class

Circumstantial evidence: Jim had vowed that the senior class would win the spirit week competition. He had all the seniors wear their jackets to show team spirit.

Forensics Lab Results

Evidence from the crime scene: Evidence bag with remaining brownie pieces, evidence bag with hairs from the coat, cheek swabs from the four suspects

Techniques to be used: DNA isolation, DNA fingerprinting

DNA Analysis

1. DNA was isolated from the hair sample, saliva sample, and cheek cell samples from each of the suspects. DNA sequences for each of the samples are listed below.

Saliva DNA sample:

ATGTAGACTGGACCATATTACGATTAG
GCACTCATTAGCCGTACAGTACTCACC

Fragment lengths:

Hair DNA sample:

ATCTCGTGACATTACCTTGTATCGATT
AGCAATTAAGGATCCTGCAGTAGCACC

Fragment lengths:

Suspect 1 DNA sample:

ATTAACGGGTATCTTCGGATTACGGAG
ACTAAGTGCCTAGATTACGAAGCTACC

Fragment lengths:

2 base pairs (bp), 18 bp, 22 bp, 12 bp

Suspect 2 DNA sample:

ATCAGCATGTGTTCAATTAGCCGAGAT
TAAGGCCACTGGAGTACTACGGCCACC

Fragment lengths:

Suspect 3 DNA sample:

ATGTAGACTGGACCATATTACGATTAG
GCACTCATTAGCCGTACAGTACTCACC

Fragment lengths:

Suspect 4 DNA sample:

ATCTCGTGACATTACCTTGTATCGATTA
GCAATTAAGGATCCTGCAGTAGCACC

Fragment lengths:

2. The next step is to cut the DNA with restriction enzymes.

   - Restriction enzymes used in this step cut DNA at the same specific site every time. Why is this essential for the procedure?

     _____

     _____

   - The restriction enzyme you are using always cuts at the sequence *ATTA*. It always cuts between the *T*s. Draw a line through each cut site in the sequences shown on page 64. (Suspect 1 is done for you as an example.)

3. Count the number of base pairs in each of the fragments you have created in your DNA strands. Record the fragment lengths under the samples. (Suspect 1 is done for you as an example.)

4. The DNA fragments are sorted by loading each sample of DNA into the well of a gel. An electric current moves the negatively charged DNA fragments toward the positive end of the gel, sorting them by size with the smaller pieces moving the farthest. This creates a unique pattern, or DNA fingerprint. Sort the DNA fragments and draw them in the gel box by their fragment length. (Suspect 1 is done for you as an example.)

5. The next step is to transfer the DNA to a nylon sheet or filter paper and incubate it with radioactive probes.

   - Explain why this step is essential in the DNA fingerprinting sequence.

     _____

     _____

6. The final step is to analyze the fingerprints of the suspects and the crime scene evidence.

Gel Box						
	Saliva	Hair	Suspect 1	Suspect 2	Suspect 3	Suspect 4
30						
29						
28						
27						
26						
25						
24						
23						
22			▬			
21						
20						
19						
18			▬			
17						
16						
15						
14						
13						
12			▬			
11						
10						
9						
8						
7						
6						
5						
4						
3						
2			▬			
1						

The Analysis

1. According to the DNA evidence, who committed the crime?

   _____

2. How do you know this person committed the crime?

   _____

   _____

   _____

   _____

3. Using the DNA evidence, explain how DNA fingerprinting can be used to clear a person as a suspect even though circumstantial evidence places him at the scene of the crime.

   _____

   _____

   _____

   _____

4. Why was Suspect 2's DNA fingerprint not identical to Suspect 3's DNA fingerprint, although they are identical twins?

   _____

   _____

   _____

   _____

5. What are some limitations to using this technique as evidence in a trial?

   _____

   _____

   _____

   _____

   _____

   _____

8 Creationism: My Beliefs and Their Defense

Introduction

It is one thing to read and hear about Creation and quite another to know what you believe. It is one thing to know what you believe and still another to defend your position. In this exercise you are asked to state your position on various Creationist topics and to give your reasons for taking these positions. As you do this lab, think about how you would use this information to help a person who has not been taught about Creation or has not taken the time to think through it.

> ### Goals
> ✓ Think through information about Creation and decide on a biblical position
> ✓ Defend a position on Creationism biblically and logically

> ### Materials
> a Bible

⌂ My Creationist Creed

A creed is a short statement of belief. It normally lists, without explanation, what a person (or group) believes. Of course, for a Christian, any creed must reflect biblical positions. In the space below, write your personal creed regarding Creationism. Using your own words, cover the main aspects of this view. After each statement, list in parentheses the Scripture passages that support it.

I believe _____

_____

_____

_____

_____

⌂ My Answers to Some Evolutionist Statements

Below are several statements frequently used to defend evolutionary theory. Based on the information you find in Chapter 8 and other areas in the text (as well as outside references if necessary), answer the following arguments with logical, scientific, and if possible, scriptural statements. Use additional paper if necessary.

1. According to many evolutionists, reptiles are the evolutionary ancestors of birds. Microscopic examination shows that scales and feathers have a similar chemical composition. Evolutionists use this fact to support their argument that scales evolved into feathers. Evolutionists disregard the fact that there is no fossil evidence of such evolution; they claim that fossils of feather evolution simply have not been located. What arguments would you use to support the Creationist position that birds did not evolve from reptiles?

_____

_____

_____

_____

_____

_____

_____

2. A visit to the zoo confirms that man shares many characteristics with the primates, especially the great apes. Evolutionists are quick to point out these uncanny similarities. They also delight in the fact that we share 98% of our DNA with chimpanzees. This, they say, is clear proof that we had a common ancestor. How would you refute this?

_____

_____

_____

_____

_____

_____

_____

3. Evolutionists often claim that homology indicates common ancestry. The fact that the "arms" of many vertebrates contain the same number of bones (Figure 8-11 on p. 188 in the text) is often used as an example of homology. Fish, frogs, lizards, birds, rats, monkeys, and man all have digestive systems with a liver attached to the intestine by a tube just below the stomach. Evolutionists argue that from this similarity all these organisms can be traced to a common ancestor. How would you argue against this logic?

_____

_____

_____

_____

_____

4. Almost all the mammals of Australia are marsupials (pouched mammals, such as the kangaroo and koala—see pp. 444–45 in the text). Evolutionists generally believe that these are "lower mammals" because their reproduction does not involve a placenta, which is a complex structure. Some evolutionists claim that there is no environmental pressure upon these marsupials to develop into placental forms. Because of this, these pouched mammals continue to live contentedly in Australia. What arguments can you give against the evolutionary concept that marsupials are a "lower" form?

_____

_____

_____

_____

_____

_____

_____

name: _____

section: _____ date: _____

9   The Use of Biological Keys

Introduction

Included with this laboratory exercise is *A Biological Key for Major Animal Classifications*. You will use this simplified dichotomous key to classify specimens (and some photographs or illustrations of specimens) in the laboratory. You will have a limited amount of time to correctly identify the specimens and properly record all the information regarding your identifications. Before you come to class, carefully read the instructions, study the examples, and do the samples that are presented.

> ### Goal
> ✓ Learn to use a biological key

> ### Materials
> animal specimens and photographs or illustrations

Preliminary Work

🏠 I. Read carefully the instructions on using a biological identification key in the facet "What Is It?" on pages 210–11 in your text. On page 70 is a glossary of terms used in the key. You may use this glossary while you identify organisms in the laboratory.

🏠 II. To receive credit for correctly identifying an organism, you will need to fill out all the information requested on the Specimen Identification Chart.

- The Sample Specimen Identification Chart (p. 70) is filled in for Specimen A, a leopard frog (see photo on p. 412 of the text). Check carefully to see how all the information was obtained from the Biological Key.

- The chart has also been filled in for Specimen B, a grasshopper (see illustration on p. 379 of the text).
  - ❑ Note that no subphylum for this example appears in the dichotomous key. Thus, there is a line drawn in the space marked *SP* on the Sample Identification Chart.
  - ❑ Draw a line through any blank in the Classification of Specimen column that does not apply.

- Try to identify the organisms listed below, and fill in the Sample Identification Chart for them.
  - ❑ Specimen C, the earthworm on page 360 of the text
  - ❑ Specimen D, the bass on page 399 of the text
  - ❑ Specimen E, the wolf on page 441 of the text

III. On the lab day be prepared to identify as many of the specimens as you can.

- You may use only the key and the glossary given with this exercise.

- You will have a limited amount of time.

- You must fill in the Specimen Identification Chart accurately and completely to get credit for identifying the organism.

- After completing this exercise, you should know how to use a dichotomous key, not simply be familiar with the divisions of the animal kingdom in the key. This key is highly artificial and does not contain all possible groups. The groupings will be discussed in more detail later.

Sample Specimen Identification Chart

Letter	Specimen name	Numbers from key used to identify organism	Classification of specimen*	
A	leopard frog	1, 2, 18, 19, 20, 24, 25	K: Animalia C: Amphibia P: Chordata O: Anura SP: Vertebrata	
B	grasshopper	1, 2, 3, 5, 10, 12, 13, 15, 16	K: Animalia C: Insecta P: Arthropoda O: Orthoptera SP: ——	
C	earthworm		K: C: P: O: SP:	
D	bass		K: C: P: O: SP:	
E	wolf		K: C: P: O: SP:	

*Key to symbols used: K: Kingdom   P: Phylum   SP: Subphylum   C: Class   O: Order

Glossary for Key to Major Animal Classifications

Abdomen: A body region posterior to (below or behind) the thorax in arthropods

Asymmetry: Lack of correspondence of body parts as a result of different shapes, sizes, and structures (animal cannot be divided into like external halves)

Bilateral symmetry: Matching external right and left sides (animal can be divided into matching halves)

Cnidocyte: A stinging cell, characteristic of cnidarians, that contains poisonous barbs, coiled threads, or a sticky substance

Dorsal: Toward the back or upper side of an animal

Epidermal plates: Small, hard plates joined beneath the epidermis to give shape and support

Exoskeleton: A system of external plates that protects and supports the animal

Gill: A respiratory structure in aquatic organisms through which oxygen and carbon dioxide are exchanged

Notochord: A tough, flexible rod of cartilage, usually located along the dorsal side of an animal; supports the animal's body

Radial symmetry: Animal can be externally divided in half like a pie; has no right or left side

Tentacle: A long, slender, movable extension of an animal's body

Terminal end: The extreme end of an animal's body

Trunk: A flexible extension of an animal's head used for grasping, feeding, and breathing

Ventral: Toward the underside, or "stomach side," of an animal

A Biological Key for Major Animal Classifications

This key deals with adult animals, not immature or larval forms. This simplified key is not designed to cover every possible organism, but it should help you understand the use of dichotomous keys. It is not a field guide and should be used to identify organisms only in this laboratory exercise.

1. Autotrophic, perhaps producing flowers and seeds.................................... **Kingdom Plantae**

    Heterotrophic, not producing flowers and seeds .... 2 .... **Kingdom Animalia**

2. No backbone (an invertebrate)... 3

    Backbone (a vertebrate) or notochord... 18 .... **Phylum Chordata**

3. Radial symmetry.. 4

    Asymmetrical or with bilateral symmetry.................................... 5

4. Soft body, usually transparent; thin tentacles; body with
    cnidocytes .... **Phylum Cnidaria**

    Firm body with internal support; covered with epidermal
    plates that often have spines; tiny hollow tube feet protruding
    from openings in the body covering that are used for
    movement.. **Phylum Echinodermata**

5. Exoskeleton .... 10 .... **Phylum Arthropoda**

    No exoskeleton; external shell or soft shell-less body.................. 6

6. External shell .... 7 .... **Phylum Mollusca**

    No external shell 8

7. Coiled shell.. **Class Gastropoda**

    Shell of two similar parts .... **Class Bivalva**

8. Wormlike body without sensory tentacles on head .... **Phylum Annelida**

    Nonwormlike body, or sensory tentacles on head........................ 9 .... **Phylum Mollusca**

9. Wormlike body with sensory tentacles on head........................... **Class Gastropoda**

    Nonwormlike body, but eight or more tentacles used for
    grasping.. **Class Cephalopoda**

10. More than three pairs of legs... 11

    Three pairs of walking legs.. 12 .... **Class Insecta**

11. Four pairs of walking legs, body in two divisions .... **Class Arachnida**

    More than four pairs of walking legs; perhaps large pincers
    on some legs; often with large, segmented abdomen; usually
    aquatic.. **Subphylum Crustacea**

12. Wings 13

    No wings 17

13. Only transparent wings.. 14

    Nontransparent wings... 15

14. Capable of inflicting sting with last abdominal segment .... **Order Hymenoptera**

    Not capable of inflicting sting (may be able to bite) .... **Order Diptera**

15. Large, often colorful wings covered with scales that easily
    rub off .... **Order Lepidoptera**

    Thick, hard, or leathery wings 16

16. Pair of hard wings covering a folded pair of thin, transparent wings .... **Order Coleoptera**

Pair of leathery wings covering a pair of straight, thin, transparent wings .... **Order Orthoptera**

17. Piercing, sucking mouthparts for obtaining blood .... **Order Siphonaptera**

Chewing mouthparts .... **Order Hymenoptera**

18. No vertebrae (backbone) .... **Subphylum Cephalochordata**

Vertebrae (backbone) .... **19** .... **Subphylum Vertebrata**

19. Jaws or beak **20**

No jaw or beak .... **Class Agnatha**

20. Skin is covered with scales **21**

Skin lacks scales **24**

21. Fins; breathing by means of gills **22**
No fins; breathing by means of lungs .... **23** .... **Class Reptilia**

22. Mouth on ventral (lower) side of body .... **Class Chondrichthyes**

Mouth at terminal (most anterior) end of body .... **Class Osteichthyes**

23. Legs or legless, no dorsal (top) or ventral (bottom) shell .... **Order Squamata**

Legs, and dorsal (top) and ventral (bottom) shell .... **Order Testudinata**

24. Skin is naked (no hair, scales, or feathers) and moist .... **25** .... **Class Amphibia**

Skin with feathers or hair **26**

25. Tail .... **Order Caudata**

No tail .... **Order Anura**

26. Body covered with feathers .... **Class Aves**

Body covered with hair .... **27** .... **Class Mammalia**

27. Hooves **28**

No hooves **29**

28. Odd number of toes, each with a hoof .... **Order Perissodactyla**

Even number of toes, each with a hoof .... **Order Artiodactyla**

29. Eats other animals **30**

Eats vegetable matter **31**

30. Lives on land .... **Order Carnivora**

Fishlike bodies, some with blowholes .... **Order Cetacea**

31. Enlarged front teeth for gnawing **32**

No enlarged front teeth for gnawing **33**

32. Legs suitable for crawling .... **Order Rodentia**

Hind legs suitable for jumping .... **Order Lagomorpha**

33. Enlarged trunk, used for breathing and for grasping .... **Order Proboscidea**

Tendency to stand erect on two hind limbs .... **Order Primates**

Specimen Identification Chart

#	Specimen name	Numbers from key used to identify organism	Classification of specimen*	
			K:	C:
			P:	O:
			SP:	
			K:	C:
			P:	O:
			SP:	
			K:	C:
			P:	O:
			SP:	
			K:	C:
			P:	O:
			SP:	
			K:	C:
			P:	O:
			SP:	
			K:	C:
			P:	O:
			SP:	
			K:	C:
			P:	O:
			SP:	
			K:	C:
			P:	O:
			SP:	
			K:	C:
			P:	O:
			SP:	
			K:	C:
			P:	O:
			SP:	

*Key to symbols used: K: Kingdom   P: Phylum   SP: Subphylum   C: Class   O: Order

Specimen Identification Chart

#	Specimen name	Numbers from key used to identify organism	Classification of specimen*
			K: C: P: O: SP:
			K: C: P: O: SP:
			K: C: P: O: SP:
			K: C: P: O: SP:
			K: C: P: O: SP:
			K: C: P: O: SP:
			K: C: P: O: SP:
			K: C: P: O: SP:
			K: C: P: O: SP:
			K: C: P: O: SP:

*Key to symbols used: K: Kingdom   P: Phylum   SP: Subphylum   C: Class   O: Order

name: _____

section: _____ date: _____

10a Bacterial Basics

Introduction

In this laboratory exercise several types of living bacteria will be cultured under laboratory conditions. These cultures will be prepared in one day, and then they will be observed twenty-four, forty-eight, and seventy-two hours later. The instructor will set up the laboratory cultures as a demonstration. You will observe these cultures and record the observations during the first few minutes of class for the next several days.

The species of bacteria used in this lab are nonpathogenic; however, if a culture becomes contaminated with bacteria from the air, pathogenic bacteria could be cultured. Therefore, you must handle live bacteria only under the instructor's supervision. **Under no circumstances should any student open any bacterial culture in the laboratory without the presence and supervision of the instructor.** You can easily make your observations for this laboratory exercise through the glass of the culture container.

Materials Used in Culturing Bacteria

Carefully observe the following pieces of equipment in the laboratory. You should be able to recognize them and know what they are used for.

Equipment

- The **petri dish**, a flat dish with a flat lid, is used for culturing bacteria, molds, and similar organisms on solid culture media.

- The **autoclave**, a piece of equipment used to sterilize materials for culturing bacteria, normally contains a closed chamber that can be heated and will keep its contents under pressure. Adequate heat and pressure will kill even spores.

- The **incubator**, a piece of equipment containing a chamber that can be kept at a specific temperature, is used to culture organisms such as bacteria.

- A **culture slant** is a test tube of solid culture medium that has been cooled at an angle, forming a large surface area of the culture medium on which to grow bacteria.

- A **transfer loop** is a piece of wire with a small loop at one end and a handle on the other. The wire can be heated to destroy bacteria on it and sterilize it. The loop can then be used to transfer bacteria from one culture to another without contamination.

Goals

✓ Observe the laboratory techniques for handling and culturing bacteria in an experiment

✓ Observe bacterial growth rates under different conditions

✓ Observe different types of bacteria

Materials

petri dishes
agar
nutrient agar (beef extract, peptone)
test tubes
transfer loop
Bunsen burner
pipets
distilled water
cotton
autoclave
microscope
preserved slide of bacterial types
immersion oil
laboratory cultures of *Bacillus cereus, B. subtilis, Rhodospirillum rubrum, Sarcina lutea,* and *S. subflava*
incubator
divided petri dishes

Culture Media

- **Beef extract** is a paste made of beef. It serves as a nutrient source in culturing many bacteria.
- **Peptone** is a protein that has been partially digested by an enzyme or an acid. It is added to many bacterial culture media since many bacteria are not able to digest some proteins.
- **Agar** is a solidifying agent obtained from certain algae; it is used to solidify the culture media on which bacteria grow.
- **Nutrient broth** is a mixture of beef extract, peptone, and water and is used for growing certain species of bacteria in a liquid culture.
- **Broth culture** is a culture of bacteria in a fluid medium (like nutrient broth).
- **Nutrient agar** is a mixture of beef extract, peptone, water, and agar and is used for growing bacteria on a solid medium.

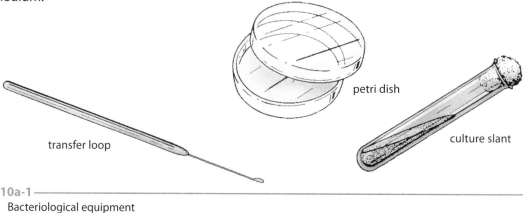

petri dish

transfer loop

culture slant

10a-1
Bacteriological equipment

Techniques Used in Culturing Bacteria

The techniques described will be demonstrated while your instructor sets up bacterial cultures for your observation.

I. Preparing the apparatus and the media

- After the proper media are set up in the proper containers, they must be sterilized in an autoclave to destroy all living materials in them.
- After the containers are removed from the autoclave, they should not be opened until it is time to transfer the culture material into them.

II. Preparing the environment

- Close windows and turn off fans and other blowers. The fewer air currents there are, the less chance there is of contamination.

III. Opening different containers of bacterial cultures

- Open a culture slant.
  - □ After opening a culture slant, pass the lip of the test tube through a flame to destroy stray bacteria.
  - □ Keep the open culture slant at an angle away from you or even parallel to the floor to avoid as much as possible having airborne bacteria settle on the agar.
  - □ Never set the cotton stopper down on a table while working with bacteria, and replace it as soon as possible.
  - □ Just before replacing the stopper, pass the lip of the test tube through a flame to destroy contaminating bacteria.
- Open a petri dish.
  - □ Open the dish only partway to avoid as much as possible having airborne bacteria settle on the agar.
  - □ When finished with the bacteria, close the petri dish as soon as possible.

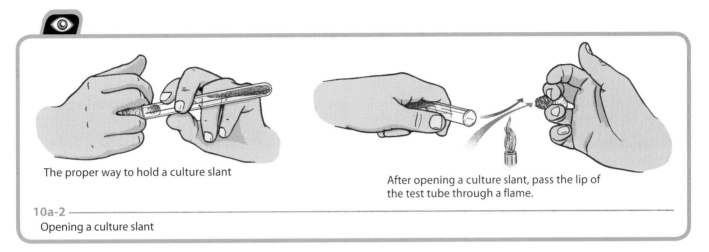

The proper way to hold a culture slant

After opening a culture slant, pass the lip of the test tube through a flame.

10a-2

Opening a culture slant

- Use a broth culture.
  - □ Broth cultures pose special problems because they cannot be held at an angle and are more easily spilled. Samples are removed using a loop or a pipet.
  - □ Take special care to leave broth cultures open as little as possible.
  - □ Pour any excess broth into a strong, bacterium-killing solvent.

IV. Transferring bacteria from one culture to another by using a transfer loop
- Heat the transfer loop in a flame until it is red-hot. This destroys any living material that may be on it. Allow the loop to cool for a few seconds.
- Touch the loop of wire at the end of the transfer loop to the bacteria being transferred.

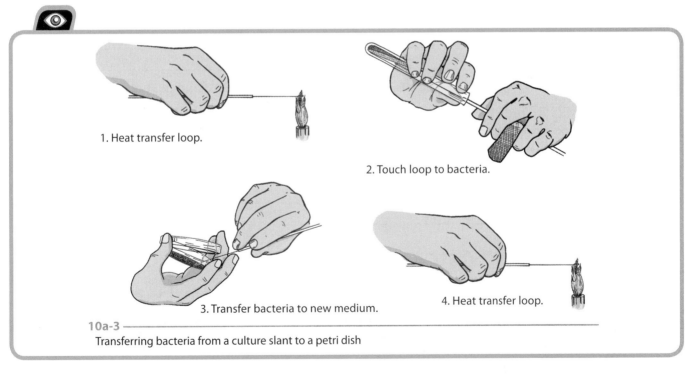

1. Heat transfer loop.

2. Touch loop to bacteria.

3. Transfer bacteria to new medium.

4. Heat transfer loop.

10a-3

Transferring bacteria from a culture slant to a petri dish

- Quickly take the transfer loop to the sterile culture medium prepared to receive the bacteria. Take care not to touch the transfer loop to the dish containing the culture medium.
- The transfer loop should be immediately heated in a flame until it is red-hot to destroy any bacteria that may be left on the loop.

Observing Bacteria

In this segment you will observe various bacterial cells and colonies through a microscope and then observe living cultures of bacteria.

I. Observe bacteria with the microscope.

- In the lab will be three microscopes on oil-immersion power (940×–1000×), each focused on a different preserved and stained bacterium.

- From your observation, decide on the type of bacterial shape and type of colony in each of the microscopes and record your answers below.

Microscope	Name and Description of Shape	Type of Colony (if any)
A		
B		
C		

II. Observe bacterial cultures.

- Observe living cultures of the following bacteria on nutrient agar. Write a detailed description of each bacterial growth, including color, size of growth, texture, shape of growth, and any other visible factors.

  - *Bacillus subtilis*: _____
  - *Rhodospirillum rubrum*: _____
  - *Sarcina lutea*: _____
  - *Sarcina subflava*: _____

- From your knowledge of etymologies and bacterial colonies and shapes, determine the shape, the type of colony, and any other characteristics each of the bacteria above has. Record your answers below.

  - *Bacillus subtilis*: _____
  - *Rhodospirillum rubrum*: _____
  - *Sarcina lutea*: _____
  - *Sarcina subflava*: _____

Bacterial Growth Rates

Two identical culture dishes, each with the same four bacteria (*Bacillus subtilis, Rhodospirillum rubrum, Sarcina lutea,* and *Sarcina subflava*), will be prepared by your instructor. They will be placed in streaks on nutrient agar in a divided petri dish. The direction of the streaks tells which bacterium is which (see Figure 10a-4). One petri dish will be kept in a dark incubator at a constant temperature around 39 °C. The other will be kept in the classroom near a window so that there will be a change in temperature and amount of light.

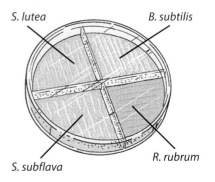

10a-4
Bacteria on a petri dish

name: _____

I. Read the questions in Section III. These are questions you will be expected to answer after three days of observing these bacteria.

II. Record your observations in the proper spaces below. (Be sure you observe thoroughly enough to answer questions later.)

If you miss an observation, obtain data from someone else in your class. You must put the person's name with the data you obtain from him, or using the information will be considered plagiarism. Because observations and methods of recording differ, data you obtain from someone else will be different in answering the questions.

In Incubator

	24 hours	48 hours	72 hours
B. subtilis			
R. rubrum			
S. lutea			
S. subflava			

In Classroom

	24 hours	48 hours	72 hours
B. subtilis			
R. rubrum			
S. lutea			
S. subflava			

III. Answer the following questions.

- Which bacterium grows the fastest in the incubator? _____

  In the classroom? _____

  If different bacteria grow best in each of these circumstances, account for this difference.

  _____

  _____

  _____

- Were there any noticeable differences in other species of bacteria grown under the different sets of conditions? ☐ yes ☐ no   If yes, what were they?

  _____

  Why would you expect differences?

  _____

  _____

- Were there any noticeable similarities in growth rates in the various species of bacteria?   ☐ yes ☐ no If yes, what were they?

  _____

  Why would you expect some species of bacteria to grow at the same rate as others?

  _____

  _____

- All these bacteria were grown on nutrient agar. Could the difference in growth rates have anything to do with the medium?   ☐ yes ☐ no

  Would it be possible for the slowest-growing bacteria in this experiment to grow faster on some other medium?   ☐ yes ☐ no   Explain your answer.

  _____

- In the growth rate experiment, what were the independent variables?

  _____

- Why is it a problem to have more than one independent variable?

  _____

  _____

- What could be done to correct this problem?

  _____

  _____

- We have considered temperature, food, and light as possible reasons that some bacteria grow faster than others. Name two other conditions that could affect the growth rate of bacteria.

  1. _____
  2. _____

- Is it possible that even if each bacterium were given optimal conditions for growth, the growth rates would still differ?   ☐ yes ☐ no   Explain.

  _____

  _____

In a typical soil sample there are millions of bacteria present. These organisms play an essential role in decomposition of organic matter, recycling it back into the environment. The end product enriches the soil and contributes to the geochemical cycles.

For either of these research questions, design an experiment using the scientific method (create a hypothesis, determine variables, set up and run the experiment, record data, analyze data, draw conclusions). Either experiment will probably require several weeks of observations.

Research question: Do organic materials decompose more quickly in regular soil or sterile soil? Sterile soil means there are no living organisms present. Soil can be sterilized with a microwave set at high power for 90 seconds for about 2 pounds of soil.

Research question: Do different organic materials decompose more rapidly than others?

10b Bacteria and Antibiotics

name: _____

section: _____ date: _____

Introduction

In this laboratory exercise a nonpathogenic species of bacterium will be exposed to several different antibiotics. Not all antibiotics are equally effective against all bacteria. Tests using antibiotic sensitivity disks are sometimes performed to reveal which antibiotic to use in fighting a particular species of bacterium. You will be able to judge the effectiveness of the different antibiotics by observing the growth of the bacteria around the antibiotic.

The species of bacterium used in this lab is nonpathogenic. The teacher will set up the culture as a demonstration. **Under no circumstance should any student open any bacterial culture in the laboratory without the presence and supervision of the instructor.** You can easily make your observations for this laboratory exercise through the clear lid of the culture container.

I. Your instructor will prepare a *sensitivity test plate*.

- A few drops of a well-mixed broth culture of *Bacillus cereus* will be poured into a sterile petri dish containing nutrient agar.

- The dish will be tilted back and forth until the entire agar surface has come in contact with the broth. This will make an even culture of *B. cereus*.

- Use forceps to place four different-colored paper disks, each containing a different antibiotic, on the moist surface of the nutrient agar and tap them lightly.

II. Read the questions in Section III that you will be asked to answer. Then record your observations in such a way that you will be able to answer the questions from them.

Goal

✓ Observe the effects of various antibiotics on bacteria

Materials

petri dish
nutrient agar
a nutrient broth culture of *Bacillus cereus*
antibiotic disks
forceps

Antibiotic Effectiveness Chart			
Antibiotic	**Color**	**24 hours**	**48 hours**

III. Answer the following questions.

- Which antibiotic most effectively prevents growth of *B. cereus*?

  _____

  Least effective?

  _____

- Do your experimental results indicate how effective these antibiotics would be against other bacteria?
  ☐ yes ☐ no Explain.

  _____

  _____

  _____

  _____

- What clinical advantage might be gained by preparing an antibiotic sensitivity test plate of an unknown throat bacterium suspected of causing sore throats?

  _____

  _____

  _____

- Pharmaceutical companies are constantly developing new antibiotics because the existing ones seem to lose their effectiveness over a period of time. From a genetic standpoint, explain why this occurs.

  _____

  _____

  _____

  _____

  _____

10c Epidemic ALERT

Introduction

Communicable diseases have had a huge impact on society both in the present and in the past. Diseases can spread from person to person by either direct or indirect methods. *Epidemiology* is the study of the spread, cause, and incidence of disease within the human population. Epidemiologists often have the task of identifying the source of a disease and its mode of transmission (how it is transmitted). By determining these factors, these scientists can suggest ways to slow the spread of the disease and possibly contain it before an epidemic takes place.

This exercise will demonstrate how easily a disease can be spread. First you will be part of the epidemic, and then you will play the role of an epidemiologist to determine who started the epidemic.

I. Population setup

- Wash your hands before you start the lab experiment.

- Obtain a numbered test tube with an unknown solution and a pipet. One test tube will have a chemical dissolved in it, the communicable disease, but as is sometimes the case, the person initially carrying the disease does not know he is contagious.

- Record the number of your test tube.

- **Test tube number** _____

II. Round 1

- Choose one person in the class to be your partner for round 1.

- Each partner will fill his pipet with solution from his own test tube.

- At the teacher's signal, place the solution in your pipet into your partner's test tube, and have your partner's solution placed into your test tube. (This action represents a handshake that could potentially transmit a microorganism.)

- Mix the contents of your test tube thoroughly.

- Record your partner's test tube number for round 1 in the space provided.

- **Partner #1** _____

III. Rounds 2 and 3

- Find a new partner for each round of the epidemic to come in contact with.

- At the teacher's signal, place the solution in your pipet into your partner's test tube, and have your partner's solution placed into your test tube.

- Mix the contents of your test tube thoroughly.

- Record your partner's test tube number for rounds 2 and 3 in the spaces provided.

- **Partner #2** _____

- **Partner #3** _____

IV. Infection analysis

- Obtain two pieces of pH paper. Test the solution in your test tube and test a sample of water.

  □ If you have been contaminated in the epidemic, the solution will test positive for a basic solution (pH ~8).

Goals

✓ Observe the simulated spread of a contagious organism in a susceptible population

✓ Model the work of an epidemiologist by analyzing data to determine the source of a disease

✓ Predict the effect of a vaccine on the epidemic activity

Materials

numbered test tubes with solution

pipet

pH test strip

□ If you have not been contaminated in the epidemic, the solution will give a neutral result, which will match the color given when you test a water sample.

- Test results: □ infected   □ not infected
- When you are finished, return the tubes and pipets and dispose of the pH paper in the trash.

V. Epidemiology work

- What type of information would be important for an epidemiologist to collect?

_____

_____

- How has technology both helped and hindered the work of an epidemiologist?

_____

_____

_____

- Obtain class data from the epidemic simulation. In the chart on page 85, write down the number of each partner that each person had in the correct order, and check the final box if the person contracted the disease.

- An epidemiologist often must work backwards from the current information to the past to determine the source of infection in an outbreak. His work is similar to that of a detective who examines a crime scene for evidence to re-create the crime and identify the perpetrator. You will need to use the contact information, starting with who ended up with the disease, to see which people came in contact and may have passed on the disease. It is a tricky problem to solve!

- Who was the source?

_____

- Briefly describe how you determined the source.

_____

- How would the results of this simulated epidemic have been affected if certain students would have been vaccinated against the disease?

_____

_____

name: _____

Test tube number	Partner #1	Partner #2	Partner #3	Sick (√ if positive test)
1				
2				
3				
4				
5				
6				
7				
8				
9				
10				
11				
12				
13				
14				
15				
16				
17				
18				
19				
20				
21				
22				
23				
24				
25				

Contact Information

- Which step simulated the transfer of microbes between people?

  _____

- What are some modes of transmission that allow microbes to spread within a population?

  _____

  _____

  _____

- What are some steps that can be taken to break the chain of infection for communicable diseases?

  _____

  _____

  _____

- In what ways would the simulated epidemic be different from a real epidemic?

  _____

  _____

  _____

- Some diseases are transmissible even before symptoms appear. How do you think incubation time (time before symptoms appear) affects the spread of the disease?

  _____

  _____

  _____

- What is the difference between an epidemic and a pandemic?

  _____

  _____

  _____

11 Protista

Introduction

Protozoans were at one time classified in the kingdom Animalia (and thus are often discussed in zoology books) in a separate phylum called Protozoa. In the modern six-kingdom system, these tiny organisms are placed in the kingdom Protista, and several of the designations that were once classes in the phylum Protozoa became phyla in the kingdom Protista (p. 257 in the text). Nutritionally, these organisms are heterotrophic, with some organisms having photosynthetic capabilities as well.

The term *algae* refers to seven phyla also in the kingdom Protista and one group of organisms in the kingdom Eubacteria (p. 224 in the text). They are often separated from the more animal-like protozoans into their own subkingdom containing the plantlike protists. Classification within the kingdom Protista is an example of why classification is an artificial system. As they are studied scientifically, the organisms are classified and then reclassified based on observable characteristics and new data. However, this does not imply a phylogenetic or evolutionary relationship of organisms in the categories but instead recognizes similarities for our convenience.

This laboratory exercise is designed to acquaint you with the major phyla of Protista. When possible, living specimens have been chosen to demonstrate the major characteristics of the phyla. Searching for, chasing, observing, drawing, and labeling living protozoans is interesting, fun, and profitable. The algal subkingdom is fascinating also, with its complexity and other evidences of design. To complete parts of this laboratory exercise, you may need to consult additional references such as a dictionary, encyclopedia, or perhaps a botany or microbiology text.

When working on this lab, keep in mind that you are responsible for each example you observe. You should know its common name (often a part of its scientific name) or Latin genus name and to what phylum it belongs, and you should be able to recognize it. Recognizing the similarities of organisms within a phylum and differences among the phyla aids you in identifying organisms. When you are asked to observe a specimen but not required to draw it, make mental notes at least. To avoid confusion regarding the phylum to which an organism belongs, it is wise to complete all the exercises for one phylum before doing another. You do not need to do the phyla in sequence.

Remember when working with this lab, a *preserved slide* is a microscope slide that has a specimen mounted on it, and a *preserved specimen*, or *mounted specimen*, is a specimen in a jar or in plastic, not designed to be used on the microscope.

Goals

✓ Observe living protozoans

✓ Compare and contrast various protozoans and protozoan phyla

✓ Observe algal specimens and note the differences among them

✓ Identify characteristics of algal classification

✓ Explain the importance of the algae as a group

✓ Identify examples of the kingdom Protista

Materials

microscope

glass slides

cover slips

living cultures of amoebas, paramecia, euglenas, *Spirogyra*, and *Protococcus*

preserved slides of amoebas, paramecia, euglenas, *Plasmodium*, desmids, diatoms, *Protococcus*, *Spirogyra*, *Spirogyra* in conjugation, dinoflagellates, and as many other protozoans and algae as possible

pipets

hand lens

glycerin or methyl cellulose

carmine powder or yeast

cotton fibers

toothpicks

forceps

scissors

preserved specimens of *Protococcus*, *Chondrus*, *Fucus*, *Corallina*, and kelp

pond water

reference books on algae and protozoans

Preliminary Work

Use information from your text to fill in these comparison charts of four phyla of the kingdom Protista, using the amoeba, paramecium, euglena, and spirogyra as representative members. After each phylum, place an X in the boxes that are under column headings that describe that phylum. Refer to these charts during the lab to compare the organisms in the areas of cellular organization, movement, feeding behavior, and reproduction.

Comparison of Basic Characteristics

	Heterotrophic	Autotrophic	Unicellular	Multicellular	Freshwater	Saltwater
Phylum Sarcodina (amoeba)						
Phylum Ciliophora (paramecium)						
Phylum Euglenophyta (euglena)						
Phylum Chlorophyta (spirogyra)						

Comparison of Reproductive Processes

	Binary fission or mitosis	Cyst formation	Conjugation
Phylum Sarcodina (amoeba)			
Phylum Ciliophora (paramecium)			
Phylum Euglenophyta (euglena)			
Phylum Chlorophyta (spirogyra)			

Comparison of Body Structures

	Flagella	Cilia	Pseudopods	Contractile vacuole	Food vacuole	Single nucleus	Micro- & macronuclei	Ecto- & endoplasm	Pellicle	Gullet	Eyespot
Phylum Sarcodina (amoeba)											
Phylum Ciliophora (paramecium)								X			
Phylum Euglenophyta (euglena)								X			
Phylum Chlorophyta (spirogyra)											

Protozoans

How to Handle Live Protozoan Cultures Properly

- Live cultures of the various protozoans are not "pure"; that is, there are other organisms in the culture. Do not be surprised if you see some unidentifiable organisms on your slide. Do not spend much time with these other organisms.
- Cultures sometimes turn "sour"; that is, the cultured organisms die.
  - □ If this happens, or if for some reason living cultures are not available to you, examine a preserved slide of the organism.
  - □ If you use a preserved slide, answer questions dealing with live observation by researching in your text.
- Care for the cultures properly.
  - □ Keep the lids on the culture dishes. (Lids, however, should not be screwed on tightly.)
  - □ Use each pipet for only one culture dish. Do not mix the pipets. Contaminating one culture with another often leads to souring.
  - □ Do not take the cultures to your desk.
  - □ Keep slides and cover slips clean and free of soap film.

Phylum Sarcodina

The phylum Sarcodina contains those unicellular organisms that move using pseudopods. We will examine the amoeba (*Amoeba proteus* or a similar species) as an example. Actually, there is considerable diversity among members of this phylum, but the typical amoeba clearly shows the major phylum characteristics.

The Amoeba

I. Prepare and observe a wet mount of living amoebas by following these instructions.

- Obtain an amoeba and prepare a wet mount from its culture.
  - □ Amoebas usually stay close to the bottom of the culture or crawl on some object.
  - □ Amoebas can be drawn into a pipet.
    - ◆ Squeeze the bulb of a pipet in the air.
    - ◆ Place the pipet directly above the place where the amoeba should be.
    - ◆ Release the bulb to suck up *one drop*.
    - ◆ Quickly put the entire drop on the slide.
  - □ Wait a minute before placing the cover slip on top of the amoeba culture on your slide. This allows the amoeba to attach to the slide and begin to move.
- Scan the entire slide on low power.
  - □ Scan from right to left; then move the slide a little lower and scan left to right. Repeat until you have scanned the entire slide.
  - □ Anything that moves faster than a snail's pace is not an amoeba.

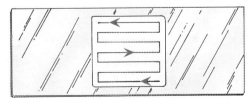

11-1

How to scan a microscope slide

- Be sure the culture medium does not evaporate. Using the pipets from the amoeba culture, add more medium to the edge of the cover slip as necessary.
- Observe the movements of the amoeba for a while on both high and low powers.
- Observe the amoebas that other students have found and let them observe yours.

- Carefully observe the cellular structures of the amoeba. Try to locate all the structures listed in the Comparison of Body Structures chart on page 88.
- You may see an amoeba engulfing food or dividing. If your amoeba appears to be doing either, inform your instructor so that you can share it with the class.

II. Answer the following questions about amoebas.

- As you observed the amoeba on your slide, what type of locomotion (movement) did the amoeba use?

_____

Describe the locomotion.

_____

- What type of cytoplasm fills the pseudopods?

_____

_____

- Is more than one pseudopod present at one time? ☐ yes ☐ no
  If so, does more than one grow at a time? ☐ yes ☐ no If so, in what circumstances?

_____

- Amoebas can respond to several types of stimuli. Describe the taxes of the amoeba. You may need to research in your text for a complete answer.

_____

_____

- Whether or not your amoeba engulfed any food particles while you observed it, describe the process of obtaining food and describe how the food is digested.

_____

_____

_____

III. Draw an amoeba in Area A.
- Draw one of the live amoebas you observed under the microscope.
- Label the drawing as completely as you can.

Other Sarcodines

I. Choose one of the following sarcodines, research it, and prepare a brief report about it (at least a half page, no more than a full page). Compare and contrast the organism to the amoeba in areas such as size, appearance, internal organization, movement, and feeding behavior. (You will need to use reference materials other than the text.)

- *Arcella*
- *Difflugia*
- *Actinosphaerium*
- *Actinophrys*
- *Globigerina*
- *Entamoeba coli*

II. If preserved slides are available, make a specimen drawing to illustrate your report.

A

Phylum Ciliophora

The phylum Ciliophora contains many diverse organisms unified by the fact that they all possess cilia. Some have cilia covering their entire body, like the paramecium, which will serve as our typical organism for the phylum. Others, like the *Vorticella*, have only a band of cilia. Some ciliates are found in sewage, some in only acidic water, some in clean ponds, and others in our bodies.

The Paramecium

I. Study a wet mount of living paramecia.

- Prepare a wet mount from the paramecium culture. Paramecia may be found throughout the culture.
- Scan the entire slide.
  - Paramecia move rapidly and will need to be chased across the slide.
  - The box below contains three methods you can use to slow down or stop your paramecium. Use the method your instructor designates.
- Be careful not to confuse other protozoans in the culture with paramecia. A paramecium looks like the slipper-shaped illustration in your text and is easy to recognize.
- Observe the paramecia on both high and low powers. Observe the paramecia that other students have found and let them observe yours.

Methods of Slowing Protozoan Movement

Cover Slip Pressure

1. As the culture medium evaporates, the cover slip will press on the organism and slow its movement.
2. A paper towel on the edge of the cover slip can be used to speed the process. Your lab partner can draw off small portions of water while you chase the organism.
3. Do not permit the medium to evaporate completely. Replenish it by placing a drop of medium beside the cover slip and letting some of it seep under the cover slip.

Cotton Fibers

1. Before you place the cover slip on the medium, you can place a small quantity of cotton fibers on the medium.
2. These serve as obstacles, blocking the path of protozoans and thus localizing their activities.

Thicker Medium

1. Special media (glycerin, methyl cellulose, or commercially prepared products) can be used to slow protozoans.
2. Because these media are thicker than water, the protozoans must move more slowly through them.

- Carefully observe the cellular structures of the paramecium. Try to locate all the structures belonging to the paramecium discussed in the Comparison of Body Structures chart on page 88.
- Sometimes paramecia can be seen during fission or conjugation. If a paramecium appears to be doing either function, inform your instructor so that you can share the observation with the class.

II. Observe various functions of the paramecium.

- Observe the reaction of paramecia to obstacles.
  - If you do not have cotton fibers in your wet mount, remove the cover slip carefully and place a few cotton fibers under the cover slip. (This observation can be done only if the paramecium is not in a thickened medium.)

□ Carefully observe the movement of the paramecium in response to the cotton fibers.

♦ Describe the movement of the paramecium. (Be sure to include the names of the cellular structures involved in its movement.)

_____

_____

♦ How does amoeboid movement compare to paramecium movement?

_____

_____

♦ By its response to the cotton, would you say the paramecium has taxes? ☐ yes ☐ no
Explain.

_____

• Observe the operation of the contractile vacuole.

□ Look carefully at a resting or confined paramecium and observe the contractile vacuole in operation. Describe what this looks like.

_____

_____

□ Could the paramecium survive if the contractile vacuole malfunctioned? Why?

_____

_____

• With a toothpick, place a few grains of carmine powder or yeast on your slide.

□ When the paramecium takes in food, it takes in the carmine powder also.

□ Trace the path of the powder or yeast as it enters the paramecium and moves within it.

♦ How do paramecia obtain their food?

_____

♦ After they have obtained food, what process of digestion do paramecia use? Explain.

_____

_____

III. Describe reproduction in paramecia.

• Describe the process of conjugation (sexual reproduction) in paramecia.

_____

_____

• Describe binary fission (asexual reproduction) in paramecia.

_____

_____

IV. Draw a paramecium in Area B.

• Draw one of the live paramecia you observed with the microscope.

• Label the drawing as completely as you can.

Other Ciliates

I. Choose one of the following ciliates, research it, and prepare a brief report about it (at least a half page, no more than a full page). Compare and contrast the organism to the paramecium in areas such as size, appearance, internal organization, movement, and feeding behavior. (You will need to use reference materials other than your text.)

- *Prorodon*
- *Stentor*
- *Colpoda*
- *Halteria*
- *Tetrahymena*
- *Vorticella*

II. If preserved slides are available, make a specimen drawing to illustrate your report.

B

Phylum Sporozoa

The phylum Sporozoa contains organisms that, as adults, lack methods of movement. (Frequently, stages in their cycle may have pseudopods or other forms of movement.) They also form spores at some stage in their life cycles. They are all parasitic and often have complex life cycles. The *Plasmodium*, which is responsible for malaria, will be the organism we study as an example of this phylum.

I. Study carefully the life cycle of the *Plasmodium* on page 261 of your text.

II. Observe a preserved slide of the various stages of the *Plasmodium* life cycle.

Algae

I. Algae classification

- At one time algae were classified in the kingdom Plantae. Identify two characteristics of algae that would have made this the logical classification for most algae.

    1. _____
    2. _____

- All of the algal phyla other than the blue-green algae are classified in the kingdom Protista. Provide a cellular characteristic that prevents algae in the kingdom Protista from being classified as plants.

    _____

- Under the present system of classification, one group of algae is placed in the kingdom Eubacteria. What characteristics place blue-green algae (cyanobacteria) in this kingdom?

    _____

- One of the major differences among the algal phyla is the color pigments found with the chlorophyll, which often give the algae found in nature slightly different colors.

II. Vocabulary study

- What are phytoplankton?

    _____

- The vegetative body of an alga that is not differentiated into leaves, roots, and stems is called the _____.

- What is a holdfast? _____
- What are sessile algae? _____
- Long, chainlike colonies of algae are called _____.
- What is a pyrenoid, and what does it do? _____

  _____

- The physical breakage of an algal colony to form two colonies is called _____.
- Identical gametes that unite to form a zygote are called _____.
- What are heterogametes? _____
- What is conjugation? _____
- A spore formed by the union of gametes is called a(n) _____.
- What is a zoospore? _____

Phylum Euglenophyta

The flagellates are unusual because many of them are heterotrophic, such as *Trypanosoma*, and classified as protozoans in the phylum Zoomastigina. Others are photosynthetic and placed with the algae in Euglenophyta, as is
our typical organism, the euglena. The euglena is a small organism compared to the amoeba and the paramecium
we have previously studied, but it is easier to find on a slide because most laboratory cultures of euglena are more
densely populated.

The Euglena

R E O

I. Observe wet mounts of living euglenas.

- Prepare a wet mount from a euglena culture. Euglenas will be found throughout the entire culture.
- Scan the slide. Euglenas can move rapidly but usually will not leave the microscope field very rapidly. Occasionally it will be necessary to use cover slip pressure or a thicker medium to slow their movement.
- Observe the euglenas on both high and low powers. Observe the euglenas that other students have found,
  and let them observe yours.
- Carefully observe the cellular structures of the euglena. Try to locate the structures belonging to the euglena discussed in the Comparison of Body Structures chart on page 88.

R E O

II. Answer the following questions concerning euglenas.

- Describe the two types of movement euglenas can have.

  1. _____
  2. _____

- Were you able to observe these two types of movement? ☐ yes ☐ no

  What cellular characteristics allow them to use these types of motion?

  _____

  _____

- Euglenas are identified as both heterotrophs and autotrophs. Explain how euglenas use these two methods
  to survive.

  _____

  _____

- What type of asexual reproduction do euglenas have? _____
- What type of sexual reproduction do they have? _____

III. Draw a euglena in Area C.

- Draw one of the live euglenas you observed under the microscope in detail.
- Label the drawing as completely as you can.

C

D

Phylum Chlorophyta

Chlorophyta, the green algae, is a large phylum. It contains many varied species. Some are tiny, microscopic spheres; others have unusual geometric shapes. Some of these unicellular algae float; others have flagella and swim toward the light. A few even thrive in snow drifts in the spring. The larger, filament-forming varieties are the usual components of "pond scum," the mat of green, slimy threads that forms on the top of many nutrient-rich water supplies. Microscopic observations of these organisms reveal fascinating structures.

Protococcus

I. *Protococcus* is unusual because it frequently lives on tree bark or on the surface of moist soil. Observe a mounted specimen of *Protococcus*.

II. Observe *Protococcus* through a microscope.

- If a living culture is available, prepare a wet mount of the culture and observe it on high and low powers.
- If a living culture is not available, observe a preserved slide of the organism.

III. In Area D draw three or four cells of this alga, labeling cell walls, chloroplasts, and any other cellular structures you find.

Spirogyra

I. Observe *Spirogyra* through a microscope.

- If a living culture is available, prepare a wet mount.
  - Place a drop of culture medium on a slide.
  - Using forceps and scissors, cut a few short strands of *Spirogyra* and place them on the slide.
  - Be careful to observe cells that are not crushed or broken.
- If a living culture is not available, use a preserved slide.

II. Make a specimen drawing in Area E of a normal filament of *Spirogyra*.

   • The filament should be three to five cells long.

   • Draw the filament, showing how the cells are joined.

   • Label the following if possible: sheath, cytoplasm, chloroplast, pyrenoid, and nucleus.

III. Observe a preserved slide of *Spirogyra* in conjugation.

   • Make a specimen drawing in Area F of *Spirogyra* in conjugation.

   • Label all the following parts and stages: conjugation tube, zygote, zygospore, empty cell, filament, and normal cell.

Desmids

   I. Observe a preserved slide of desmids.

   II. Draw in Area G the outlines of five different shapes of desmids found on the slide.

   III. Give one structural difference between desmids and diatoms.

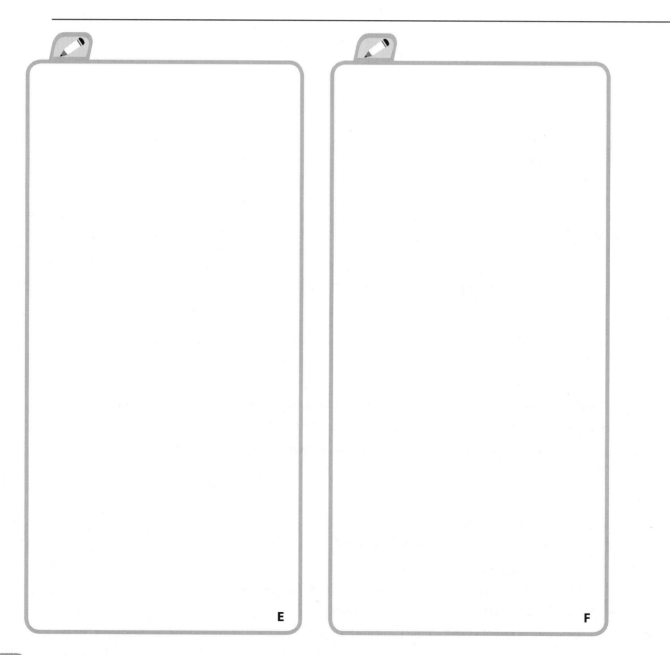

E

F

Phylum Bacillariophyta

The phylum Bacillariophyta contains the diatoms. These tiny but often intricately patterned organisms are sometimes called "glass boxes" because of their shapes and because they have silica in their cell walls.

Diatoms

I. Scan the preserved slides of diatoms and observe the various shapes.

II. Draw in Area H the outlines of five differing diatoms.

III. Diatoms have been used for many different purposes because of their hard, silica-containing cell walls. List four uses of diatom cell walls.

1. _____

2. _____

3. _____

4. _____

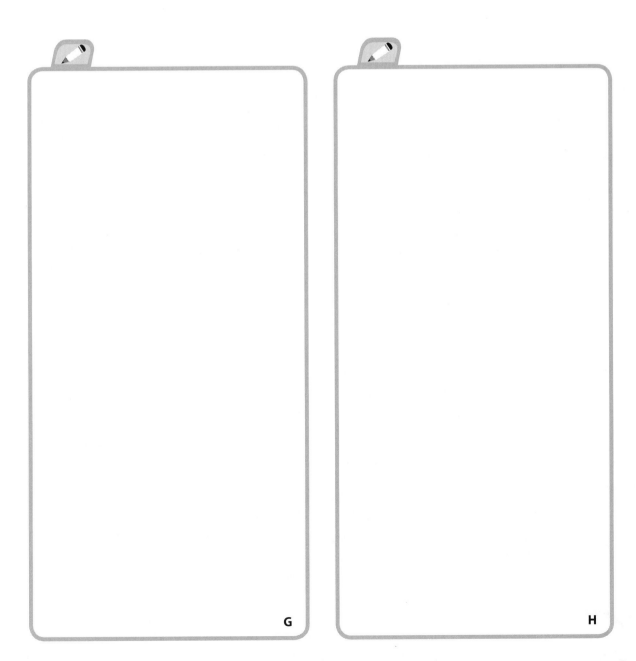

G   H

Phylum Phaeophyta

Although the phylum Phaeophyta is one of the smallest phyla in number of species, the sizes of its individual organisms more than make up for their small number. Some of the larger brown algae may have colonies more than 30 m (100 ft) long. Some areas of the ocean are almost overrun with "algae forests" made up of members of this phylum. Although these appear to be plants with large leaves and stems, they actually lack true tissues and are colonies.

Fucus

I. Observe the mounted specimen of *Fucus*.

II. Identify the receptacle and the air bladder, describing the differences between them.

	Receptacle	Air Bladder
Size		
Shape		
Location on thallus		
Function		

Kelp

I. Observe the mounted specimen of kelp.

II. Research kelp in other sources and write on your own paper a brief statement describing its appearance, use, and importance to man. Identify your sources.

Phylum Rhodophyta

Members of phylum Rhodophyta, the red algae, are multicellular and red. Most members of the phylum are marine organisms. The red algae are similar to the brown algae except for the foods they store and the pigments they contain.

Chondrus (Irish Moss)

I. Observe the preserved specimen of this marine alga in the laboratory.

 II. This alga is economically important. Research to find out what substance is derived from this alga and how it is used.

_____

_____

Corallina

I. This marine alga is important in reef formation. It extracts calcium-containing substances from seawater and deposits them in its cell walls.

II. Observe the preserved specimen of this marine alga in the laboratory.

Phylum Dinoflagellata

The dinoflagellates are often called the "fire algae" because of the reddish to yellowish color these organisms can give to water. Although many of these are harmless, some cause extensive damage.

I. Some members of this phylum have bioluminescent properties. This explains a common phenomenon that startles many when they first see it. What is this phenomenon?

_____

What are bioluminescent properties?

_____

II. Examples of dinoflagellates

- *Karenia* is a marine genus, some species of which cause the red tides of Florida. Research red tides and tell how an alga that is usually considered food can kill large quantities of fish.

_____

_____

Are algal blooms always detrimental to the environment?

_____

- *Peridinium*, a common freshwater genus, is illustrated in Figure 11-2.
  - □ Using the information in your textbook, label the following structures in Figure 11-2: flagella, groove, and cellulose plates.
  - □ Observe a preserved slide of freshwater dinoflagellates.
    - ♦ Were you able to find *Peridinium*? ☐ yes ☐ no
    - ♦ Describe two other dinoflagellates you may have seen.
      1. _____

      _____

      _____

      2. _____

      _____

      _____

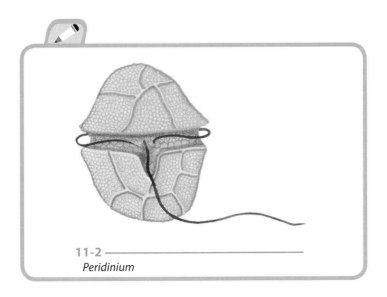

11-2 _____
Peridinium

Observing Pond Water

Although many organisms known as plankton may be found in other kingdoms, most of the easily recognizable plankton belong to the kingdom Protista. Observing pond water can be interesting and profitable. You can often see organisms that you have studied as well as unfamiliar examples of phyla that you have studied.

I. Observe pond water from the laboratory culture through a microscope.

- Make a wet mount of the material at the bottom of the culture.

- Make another wet mount of the material near the surface of the culture.

- Why is it advisable to take samples from both areas?

  _____

- Various keys and other reference books are available in the classroom for you to use in identification of the organisms you find.

- What characteristics will help you identify the organisms?

  _____

  _____

II. List each organism that you observe under the appropriate heading below.

- Organisms studied—give name and phylum.

  _____

  _____

- Organisms not studied but recognized—describe and, if possible, give names and phyla of the organisms.

  _____

  _____

- Organisms not recognized—describe and name if possible.

  _____

  _____

III. Draw in Area I several of the organisms that you found in pond water but had not studied.

- Try to find out the names of what you have and the groups to which they belong.

- Label each of your drawings as completely as possible.

12 Fungi and Lichens

Introduction

The smallest kingdom, Fungi, may seem mysterious and irrelevant since we seldom see fungi unless they have large fruiting structures. Although many are secluded in dark, musty corners or grow on dead organisms, fungi are still important organisms. They are responsible for most of the decomposition of dead organisms. Imagine the mess we would be in without that service. Also, without fungi and the enzymes they produce, we would not have bread, many cheeses, and mushrooms. That would pretty much wipe out pizza!

Occasionally you will have to research in other books for answers as you are working on this exercise. Fungi were once considered plants; therefore, most general botany texts have chapters covering fungi.

Technically, lichens are not placed in a phylum or any classification in the biological taxonomic system. Lichens are duo-organisms consisting of an alga and a fungus living together in a close relationship. In naming, the duo-organism is considered one organism and given one scientific name.

Goals
✓ Observe fungus specimens
✓ Recognize the differences among types of fungi
✓ Recognize the differences between fungi and other organisms
✓ Identify characteristics of fungal classification
✓ Observe and classify lichen specimens

Materials
microscope

stereomicroscope or hand lens

living cultures of *Rhizopus nigricans*, *Penicillium notatum*, and yeast

preserved slides of *Rhizopus nigricans*, w.m.; *R. nigricans* forming zygotes; *Penicillium*; and *Coprinus*, c.s.

preserved specimens of *Aspergillus*, puffballs, shelf fungi, mushrooms, and lichens

methylene blue

glass slides

cover slips

pipets

immersion oil

🏠 Preliminary Work

I. Answer the following questions about fungal classification and characteristics.

• What is the primary reason fungi are not classified as algae?

_____

_____

• What is the primary reason fungi are not classified as plants?

_____

• What characteristics are used to divide fungi into phyla?

_____

_____

• Give two examples demonstrating how fungi are destructive.
  1. _____
  2. _____

• Give two functions of fungi that benefit man.
  1. _____
  2. _____

II. Answer the following questions about fungal vocabulary.

• What is mycology?

_____

• What are hyphae?

_____

- What are aerial hyphae that connect groups of hyphae together called?

  _____

- What are mycelia?

  _____

- What are rhizoids?

  _____

- What part of the fungus both produces and disperses spores for sexual reproduction?

  _____

- What are haustoria?

  _____

- What is a sporangiophore?

  _____

- When spores are not in an enclosure, what is the spore-producing structure called?

  _____

- What is an ascus?

  _____

- What is a basidium?

  _____

- What are basidiospores?

  _____

Phylum Zygomycota

The phylum Zygomycota contains the organisms we normally think of as fungi. These organisms are usually sessile, produce spores, and resemble algae in structure. These fungi bear asexually produced spores in sporangia. Sexual reproduction takes place when specialized hyphae unite. Examples of this phylum are common and abundant; they are found under almost every step you take.

Rhizopus nigricans

Rhizopus nigricans is a black mold that often grows on bread.

R E O

  I. Using either a stereomicroscope or a hand lens, observe cultures of *R. nigricans*.

- Describe what you see, including any fungal structures you can identify.

  _____

  _____

- *R. nigricans* produces hyphae that are clear or white. What causes its dark appearance?

  _____

II. Observe a preserved slide of *R. nigricans*, w.m., on high power.

- Make a drawing in Area A that includes sporangiophores, sporangia, hyphae, mycelia, stolons, and rhizoids.

- Label these structures on your drawing.

III. *R. nigricans* reproduces sexually by forming zygotes by conjugation.

- Observe a preserved slide of *R. nigricans* with zygotes.

- In Area B draw a zygote with two parent hyphae.

- What is the difference between a zygote and a zygospore?

_____

_____

_____

Other Examples of Phylum Zygomycota

Choose any example of phylum Zygomycota not previously used in this exercise. Possible examples are *Pilobolus* (cap-thrower fungi), *Entomophthora* (insect parasites), and *Mucor*.

I. Observe laboratory specimens or preserved slides of your example, if possible.

II. Consult at least one other text for information about your specimen.

III. Make a drawing of your example and label it completely.

IV. Write a description of the structure, habitat, and economic significance of your specimen.

Phylum Ascomycota

The second phylum we will study is Ascomycota. Often these organisms appear very similar to the zygomycetes, but they differ in their spore-forming structures. Some of the ascomycetes, however, have varied and unusual structures.

Penicillium

Penicillium is a common mold of fruits and is the original source of the antibiotic penicillin.

I. Using either a stereomicroscope or a hand lens, observe the laboratory culture of *Penicillium notatum*. Describe what you see, including any fungal structures you can identify.

_____

_____

II. Observe a preserved slide of *Penicillium*.

- Look for conidia and conidiophores.

- On the next page are diagrams of conidia and conidiophores. Which one exhibits the structures found in *Penicillium*? ☐ Figure 12-1 ☐ Figure 12-2

A

B

- Label the diagram appropriately.

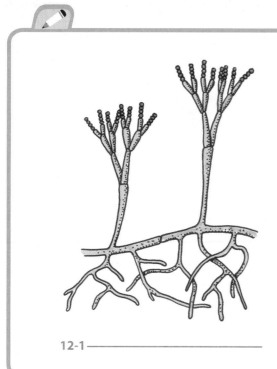

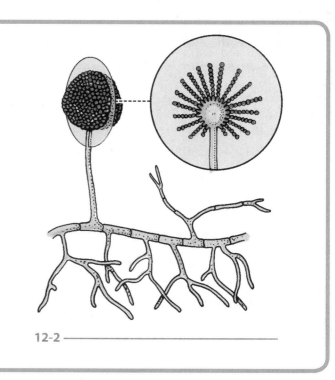

12-1 _____

12-2 _____

III. Does *Penicillium* have a use besides being a source of antibiotics? ☐ yes ☐ no

If so, what is it?

_____

Aspergillus (Powdery Mildews)

I. Observe a preserved specimen of the genus *Aspergillus*.

II. Based on your observation and reading, why is the name "powdery mildews" appropriate?

_____

_____

III. What effect do powdery mildews have on plants?

_____

Yeasts

I. A drop of yeast culture will be mixed with a stain (methylene blue) and placed on a slide for you to observe. The slide will be set up for oil-immersion viewing (1000×).

- Draw a few yeast cells in Area C. If possible, include some that are budding. Label your drawing as completely as you can.

- What type of reproduction is budding considered?

_____

- Would the new yeast cell be a clone of the one it budded from? ☐ yes ☐ no

C

Explain your answer.

_____

- Smell the yeast culture and determine whether you detect an alcohol odor. What chemical process does this odor indicate?

_____

II. What are some ways yeasts profit man?

_____

The Imperfect Fungi

Some fungi have no known form of sexual reproduction. However, as they are studied, methods of sexual reproduction are often discovered. These organisms usually end up being placed in the phylum Ascomycota because they resemble ascomycetes in many ways. They are few in number and, except those that are parasitic to man, they have only minor importance.

I. Example: **Athlete's foot**

Find information about the athlete's foot fungus. Describe the fungus itself. Then describe the common disease it causes, how the disease is spread, how it can be prevented, and how it can be cured.

_____

_____

_____

II. Example: **Ringworm**

Find information about the ringworm fungus. Describe the fungus itself. Then describe the common disease it causes, how the disease is spread, how it can be prevented, and how it can be cured.

_____

_____

_____

Other Examples of Phylum Ascomycota

Choose any example of phylum Ascomycota not previously covered in this exercise. Some examples you might like to choose from are *Neurospora*, *Taphrina*, *Morchella* (morel), cup fungi, and *Peziza*.

I. Observe laboratory specimens or preserved slides of your example, if possible.

II. Consult at least one other text for information about your specimen.

III. Draw your example and label the drawing completely.

IV. Write a description of the structure, habitat, and economic significance of your specimen.

Phylum Basidiomycota

The basidiomycetes are a widely varied group of fungi. They range from those having extremely large vegetative and fruiting bodies to others that have very small ones. Some are harmful parasites; others are saprophytes. Some contain deadly poisons; others are prized as food. A number have several hosts during their intricate life cycles.

Rusts and Smuts

I. The rusts and smuts are usually parasitic fungi with many hosts. Many of them are parasites on food crops and can be extremely harmful.

II. *Puccinia* is the genus that contains many rusts, including the common wheat rust. Compare the life cycle given in other books with the life cycle in Figure 12-3. Using the terms provided in the box next to the diagram, label the structures in the diagram.

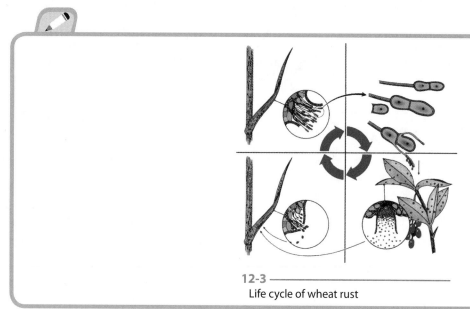

| aeciospores |
| barberry |
| basidiospores |
| basidium |
| hyphae |
| teliospores |
| urediospores |
| wheat |

12-3 ─────────────
Life cycle of wheat rust

Puffballs

Observe preserved and dried specimens of puffballs.

    I. Where are the basidia and basidiospores (spores) located on the puffballs?

_____

    II. How are the spores released?

_____

Shelf Fungi

Observe preserved specimens of shelf fungi and note differences and similarities among the various species.

    I. Where are the basidia and basidiospores located on the shelf fungi?

_____

    II. How are spores released from these fungi?

_____

Mushrooms

    I. Observe preserved specimens or fresh samples of mushrooms.

      • Note the cap, gills, stipe, and hyphae of the various species.

      • Note the different colors, sizes, and textures of the various species.

      • Label as many structures as you can in Figure 12-4.

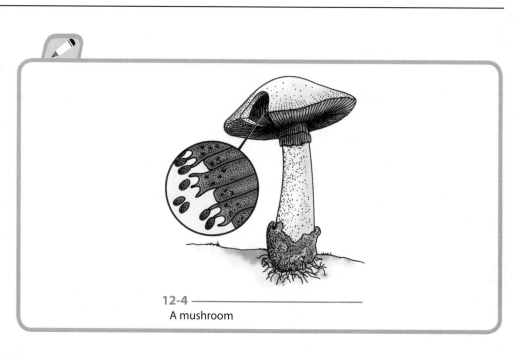

12-4 ─────────────
A mushroom

II. Observe the preserved slide of *Coprinus*, c.s. (Be sure to use the cross section of the cap.)

- Find the gills and locate the basidia and basidiospores.
- In Area D, make a drawing that includes a section of a gill with basidia and basidiospores.
- Label the drawing as completely as possible.

III. Choose any two specific mushrooms and research them in other texts. Briefly describe them, telling their habitat, importance, and a couple of unusual facts.

- Name of mushroom:

  _____

  Description:

  _____

  _____

  _____

  _____

  _____

  _____

  _____

  _____

  _____

- Name of mushroom:

  _____

  Description:

  _____

  _____

  _____

  _____

  _____

  _____

  _____

  _____

  _____

D

Other Examples of Phylum Basidiomycota

Choose any example of phylum Basidiomycota not previously covered in this exercise. Some examples you might like to choose from are earthstars, stinkhorns, apple cedar rust, and corn smut.

I. Observe laboratory specimens or preserved slides of your example, if possible.

II. Consult at least one other text for information about your specimen.

III. Draw your example and label it completely.

IV. Write a description of the structure, habitat, and economic significance of your specimen.

The Lichens

Lichens are not fungi, but they do contain fungi. Actually, they are a symbiotic set of organisms, living together as one for the benefit of both.

I. What two organisms are always found in a lichen? Trace the organisms to the correct phylum if possible.

1. _____

2. _____

II. Your instructor will supply you with several different lichen specimens labeled by letters. There will be at least one of each of the three types of lichens. Identify the type of each specimen and describe it in the chart below.

Example	Type of Lichen	Description of This Specimen
A		
B		
C		

III. In Area E, complete a drawing of the macrostructure of one of your lichen specimens.

- Identify your drawing as the appropriate type of lichen (crustose, foliose, or fruticose).

E

Inquiry Investigation

I. **Research question:** How do environmental factors (such as temperature, light, moisture, and food source) affect fungal growth?

II. **Method:** Fungi can be grown on bread as a medium. A slice of bread placed into a sealed bag will grow fungi after a period of time, usually several days.

III. **Design:** Design an experiment using the scientific method to explore fungal growth.

IV. WARNING: Fungi in the enclosed environment will form a lot of spores. To prevent inhalation of spores, do not open the bag once your experiment has started.

13a Plant Identification

Introduction

It is one thing to see plant characteristics in photographs or drawings, but it is quite another to recognize those characteristics in actual specimens. In this laboratory exercise you will list characteristics you would look for when identifying the major plant groups. You will then use this list to identify as many specimens as possible. It is not important that you know the names of any of these specimens. Your job is merely to assign them to the correct phylum or class. A thoroughly accurate list will allow you to identify more specimens and to do so more efficiently. The more specimens you correctly identify, the better your grade will be.

🏠 Preliminary Work

I. Fill in the Plant Classifications Chart on page 111.

- List characteristics for each classification, using characteristics that you can distinguish by sight. (For example, "Has cell walls made of cellulose" would be a poor characteristic to list since you cannot tell this by looking at a specimen.)

- Try to list characteristics that apply only to a particular taxonomic group. ("Has chlorophyll" would be a poor characteristic to list since nearly all plants have chlorophyll.)

- As you identify the specimens in class, you will be permitted to refer to the Plant Classifications Chart and Leaf Venations only. Put on these all the information you will need.

- You may not list names of plants on your Plant Classifications Chart or Leaf Venations.

II. Make sketches of the types of leaf venations on page 112. You may draw variations of the venations to help you as you fill in the Specimen Chart during lab.

In-Class Procedures

Various specimens will be present in the lab. Some will be fresh; others preserved. Some will be entire plants, while others will be pieces of a plant.

- Each specimen will be numbered, and you will be asked to identify it on the Specimen Chart.

- You must list your reasons for each identification by listing the letters for the appropriate characteristics from your Plant Classifications Chart. (See Sample Specimen Chart on page 110.)

- If the specimen has leaves, you must list the type of leaf venation it has to get full credit for that specimen.

- If the specimen has needles or scales, you must write *needles* or *scales* in the venation section of the Specimen Chart to get full credit for that specimen.

- Some of the specimens will have their common and/or scientific names on them. If they are not labeled, you do not need to list their names on the Specimen Chart.

Goals

✓ Learn major classifications in the plant kingdom

✓ Recognize various plant characteristics in specimens

Materials

Living and preserved plant specimens

#	Name	Classification	Reasons for identification	Venation
			Sample Specimen Chart	
1	sugar maple	Dicot	A, C, D*	s. pal.
2	iris	Monocot	A, E	parl.
3	white pine	Conif.	E	needles
4				
5				
6				
7				
8				
9				
10				
11				
12				

*Note: These letters are for example only and are not intended as accurate answers.

Plant Classifications Chart

I. Phylum Bryophyta* (*Bryo.*)**

    A. *Lacks vascular tissue; most living specimens about one inch high* _____

    B. _____

    C. _____

    D. _____

    E. _____

II. Phylum Lycophyta* (*Lyc.*)**

    A. _____

    B. _____

    C. _____

    D. _____

    E. _____

III. Phylum Pteridophyta* (*Pter.*)**

    A. _____

    B. _____

    C. _____

    D. _____

    E. _____

IV. Phylum Coniferophyta* (*Conif.*)**

    A. _____

    B. _____

    C. _____

    D. _____

    E. _____

V. Phylum Anthophyta

   • Class Monocotyledoneae* (*Monocot*)**

    A. *Leaf venation: parallel* _____

    B. _____

    C. _____

    D. _____

    E. _____

   • Class Dicotyledoneae* (*Dicot*)**

    A. *Leaf venation: pinnate or palmate* _____

    B. _____

    C. _____

    D. _____

    E. _____

*Use only these levels of classification when identifying the specimens.

**The abbreviations in parentheses may be used when filling in the Specimen Chart.

Leaf Venations†

Parallel (parl.)‡

Simple palmate (s. pal.)‡

Palmately compound (pal. c.)‡

Simple pinnate (s. pin.)‡

Pinnately compound (pin. c.)‡

Bipinnately compound (bipin.)‡

†It is suggested that you draw a couple of modifications of the leaves (heavily lobed, etc.) so that you can more easily recognize them. When identifying succulent leaves, you may have to make an educated guess. Succulent leaves are often very thick, and the venation does not show.

‡You may use the abbreviations in parentheses as you fill in the Specimen Chart.

		Specimen Chart		
#	Name	Classification	Reasons for identification	Venation
1				
2				
3				
4				
5				
6				
7				
8				
9				
10				
11				
12				
13				
14				
15				
16				
17				
18				
19				
20				
21				
22				
23				
24				
25				
26				
27				
28				
29				
30				
31				
32				
33				
34				
35				

#	Name	Classification	Reasons for identification	Venation
36				
37				
38				
39				
40				
41				
42				
43				
44				
45				
46				
47				
48				
49				
50				
51				
52				
53				
54				
55				
56				
57				
58				
59				
60				
61				
62				
63				
64				
65				
66				
67				
68				
69				
70				
71				
72				

13b Plant Organs

Introduction

Plants have their own ways of handling the basic functions necessary for survival. Observing some of their special structures will help you understand the functions of leaves, roots, and stems.

Leaves

Plant leaves are usually the major photosynthetic organs of the plant. Foliage leaves, which are the type you will work with in this exercise, display the typical characteristics of leaves. We will note some of the varieties of foliage leaves and then observe their specialized design for carrying on photosynthesis.

 Gross Structure

  I. Study leaf venations.

  - Make a collection of leaves typical of the various types of leaf venations.

  - Press and mount your leaves on paper, one type per page. You may have several specimens with the same type of leaf venation on the same page.

  - On each page write the common names of the specimens you have collected and the names of several other plants with the same type of leaf venation.

  - You should have examples of the following types if possible:
    - □ parallel
    - □ simple pinnate, pinnately compound, bipinnately compound
    - □ simple palmate, palmately compound
    - □ scales
    - □ needles
    - □ modified leaves such as bracts and spines

 II. Study leaf margins and shapes.

  - Make a collection of leaves with different margins and shapes.

  - Press and mount your leaves on paper, one type of leaf margin or leaf shape per page. You may have several specimens with the same type of margin or shape on the same page.

  - On each page write the common names of the specimens you have collected and list the names of several other plants with the same type of leaf margin or leaf shape.

  - You should have examples of at least the following margins:
    - □ entire
    - □ undulate
    - □ dentate
    - □ serrate

Goals

✓ Observe some of the plant organs and tissues

✓ Understand the anatomy and physiology of plant leaves, roots, and stems

Materials

collection of leaves

microscope

preserved slides of leaf, c.s.; *Ranunculus* young root, c.s.; *Ranunculus* stem, c.s.; and *Zea* stem, c.s.

fresh spinach or geranium leaves

forceps

glass slides

cover slips

leaf with epidermal hairs

stereomicroscope or hand lens

plants rooting in water

dormant twigs

scalpel

- You should include at least the following shapes:
    - linear
    - cordate
    - deltoid
    - lobed
    - circular

Microstructure

I. In Area A, draw a cross section of a leaf from a preserved slide.

- Draw five to fifteen cells of each type of tissue (five to fifteen upper epidermal cells, five to fifteen palisade mesophyll cells adjacent to the epidermal cells, and so on). Continue until you have a section of the leaf from top to bottom, including a vein. Include guard cells and stomata if possible.
- Include a vein (not the large vein in the middle of the leaf). Try to find a vein cut in cross section, not one that has been cut longitudinally.
- Be careful not to draw a torn segment of leaf.
- Label all parts.
- How does the structure (size, shape, distribution) of cells in the palisade and spongy mesophyll contribute to their functions?

_____

_____

_____

_____

- What two tissue types are found in leaf veins? Are they both necessary? Explain.

_____

_____

_____

- If the veins of a leaf were blocked, how would this affect the plant?

_____

_____

A

II. Study and draw a wet mount of a leaf epidermis.

- Using your forceps or your fingers, carefully peel a piece of transparent lower epidermis from a geranium or spinach leaf.

- Make a wet mount of this tissue and observe the epidermis using a microscope.

- What is the position of the guard cells?
  ☐ open ☐ closed

  What does this tell you about the photosynthetic activity of the leaf at the time you took off the epidermis?

  _____

  _____

  _____

13b-1
Obtaining the lower leaf epidermis

- What is the approximate ratio of guard cells to epidermal cells in this epidermis specimen?

  _____

- Would you expect this ratio to be different in other plants? ☐ yes ☐ no

- Why or why not?

  _____

- In Area B draw a section of epidermal tissue, including two stomata with guard cells and several epidermal cells. Label your drawing completely.

III. Observe a leaf with epidermal hairs under either a stereomicroscope or a hand lens. Observe the area near the margin of the leaf. Describe what you see.

_____

_____

Roots

Roots anchor plants, help them absorb water and dissolved substances, and provide areas for storage. In this section you will observe the structures of roots that do all these functions. Carefully note which structure of the root accomplishes each function.

Gross Structure

I. On your own paper, draw schematic diagrams of a taproot system and a fibrous root system. On both root system drawings, label primary and secondary roots.

II. Structurally, most tree roots start as taproot systems but change to fibrous root systems as they grow. How does this benefit the root? (Hint: Think about the function of the root.)

B

_____

_____

_____

Microstructure

R
E
O

I. Observe the preserved slide of a young *Ranunculus* (buttercup) root, c.s. Follow these instructions.

• Scan the entire slide.

• In Area C draw a wedge-shaped section of the root (triangular, touching both the center of the root and the outside; see Figure 13b-2).

• You may need to move the slide while you make this drawing because what you are drawing is probably larger than the field of view of the microscope.

• Include all the tissues found in the root. Label all the parts.

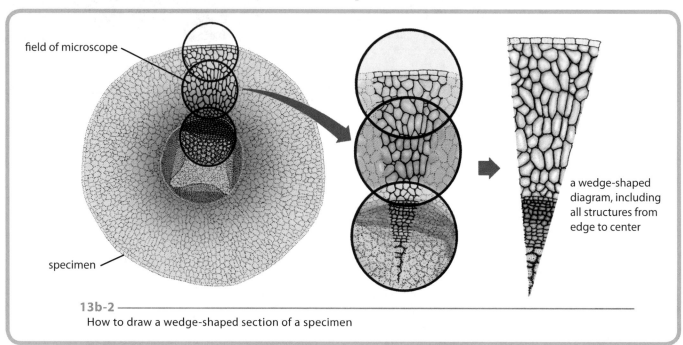

field of microscope

specimen

a wedge-shaped diagram, including all structures from edge to center

13b-2 ———
How to draw a wedge-shaped section of a specimen

R
E
O

II. With a hand lens, observe the root hairs on the maturation region of a root growing in water. (A rooting stem or a seedling may be used.)

• What is the function of the root hairs?

_____

_____

• Which root areas have root hairs?

_____

• Why are root hairs found only in certain areas?

_____

_____

_____

• What other observations did you make about root hairs?

_____

_____

C

Stems

Although some plants (such as the cactus) have stems that are the primary photosynthetic structures and even the storage organs of the plant, in this section we will observe stems that use typical structures to accomplish the usual function of manufacturing and displaying leaves.

Gross Structure

I. Observe a dormant twig section. Answer the following questions:

- My twig number is

  _____

- How many years old is the twig?

  _____

  How do you know?

  _____

  _____

- Was the rate of growth the same each year?
  ☐ yes   ☐ no   How do you know?

  _____

  _____

  _____

  _____

- What factors would have affected the growth rate of the twig?

  _____

  _____

  _____

  _____

- How many nodes were produced during the most recent growing season (last summer)?

  _____

II. Using a scalpel, make a longitudinal section of an apical (terminal) bud.

- Do not use the apical bud of any of the twigs used earlier.
- In Area D draw the dissected apical bud and label all the parts you observed.

D

Microstructure

I. Observe a preserved slide of a *Ranunculus* (buttercup) stem, c.s.

- Scan the entire slide.

- In Area E make a drawing of a wedge-shaped section of the stem (triangular, touching both the center of the stem and the outside; see Figure 13b-2). You may need to move the slide while you make the drawing because what you are drawing is probably larger than the field of view of the microscope.

- Label all the parts.

- *Ranunculus* is a dicot. Is the *Ranunculus* stem typical of this class? ☐ yes ☐ no

II. Observe the preserved slide of a cross section of a *Zea* (corn) stem.

- Follow the directions given above to make a drawing of the stem in Area F.

- *Zea* is a monocot. Is the *Zea* stem typical of this class? ☐ yes ☐ no

E

F

🏠 *On Your Own*

Lab 4 introduced a technique using leaf disks to measure the rate of photosynthesis. Design an experiment using the scientific method that would test the effects of open and closed stomata on photosynthesis. (Hint: You will need to determine a way to close the stomata in order to do this experiment.)

Design a Nature Walk Guide that incorporates the characteristics of plants you worked with in Labs 13a and 13b. Format your guide similarly to the biological key presented in Lab 9. When using your guide on a hike, you should be able to identify plants from the phyla listed on page 111 and explain why. You should also be able to identify leaf and stem characteristics.

14 Flowers, Fruits, and Seeds

Introduction

The sexual reproductive parts of angiosperms are found in structures called flowers. There are many types of flowers, but they all have certain characteristics in common. Note these characteristics as you study the flowers and their products, the fruits and the seeds.

Flowers

Not all flowers are variations of the rose, lily, or daisy. Many flowers lack showy petals and many have very unusual structures, but most of them share the same basic floral parts.

I. Observe and label the diagrams of various flowers in Figure 14-1 on pages 122–23.

- On each diagrammed flower, label as many of the following structures as you can: carpel, stigma, style, ovary, ovule, stamen, anther, filament, pollen, petals, sepals, and receptacle. (NOTE: Not all of these are visible in all the flowers illustrated. Use your knowledge of these structures to assign the labels.)

- By the names of the various flowers in Figure 14-1, indicate whether each flower

  □ is complete or incomplete.
  □ is male, female, or both.
  □ has a superior ovary or an inferior ovary.
  □ contains a single ovule or multiple ovules.
  □ is composite or not composite.
  □ is from a monocot or a dicot.

II. Dissect a flower.

- Using your scalpel, carefully dissect a live flower to see the various internal structures. The best method of dissection is to slice through the ovary area from the top down, as seen on the drawings on the following two pages. Examine the structures with a hand lens if necessary.

- In Area A draw a longitudinal section of your flower. Label all parts.

- Indicate whether your flower is complete or incomplete; is male, female, or both; has a superior or inferior ovary; contains a single ovule or multiple ovules; is a composite flower or not a composite flower; and comes from a monocot or dicot plant.

_____

_____

_____

Goals

✓ Observe the structures of a typical flower and learn the structures of various flowers

✓ Observe various kinds of fruits and learn their parts

✓ Observe and learn the structures of a typical seed

Materials

fresh flower specimens (e.g., gladioli)

fresh fruit specimens (including at least a pome, drupe, true berry, modified berry, and a pod)

seeds

scalpel

hand lens

large kitchen knife

single-edged razor blade

A

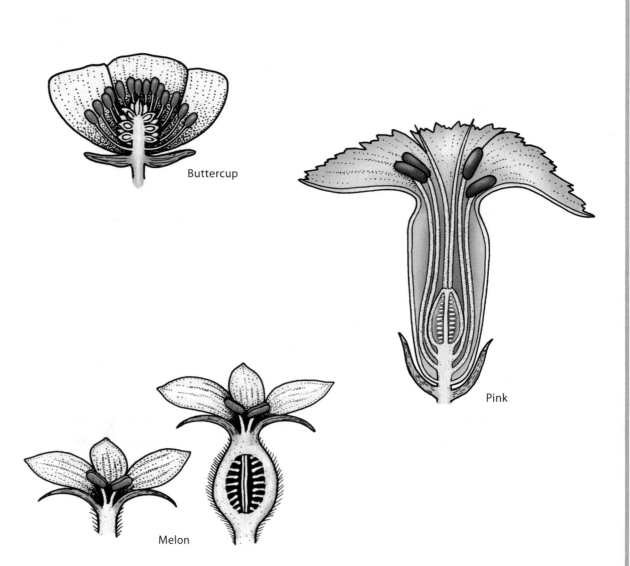

Buttercup

Pink

Melon

Raspberry

14-1
Flowers

name: _____

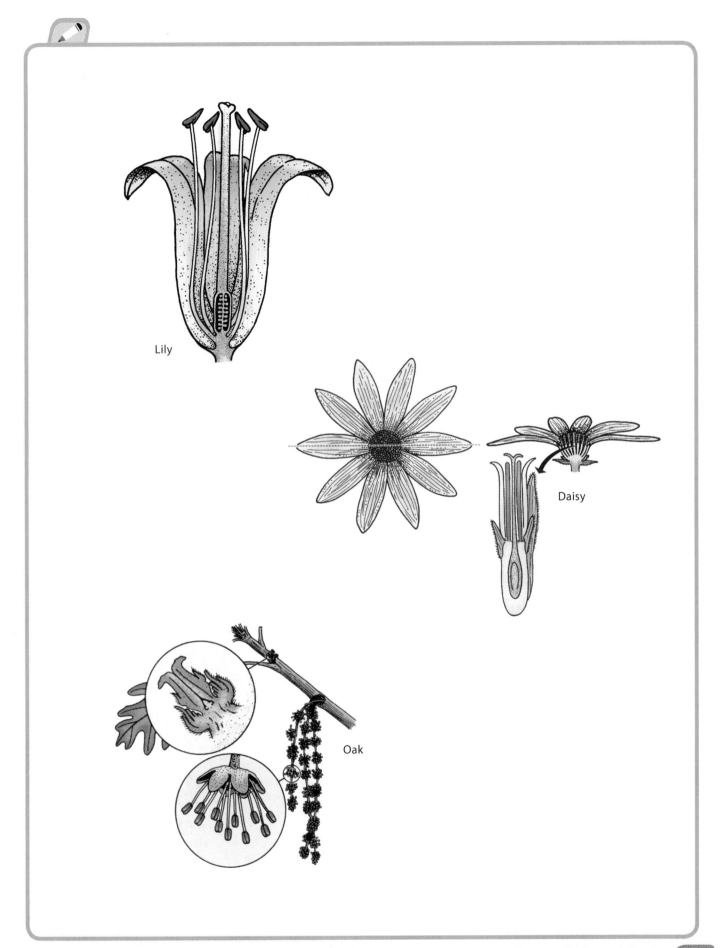

Lily

Daisy

Oak

Fruits

A fruit is a ripened ovary. Although many fruits are like the familiar apple and orange, many are quite different. Fruits have been classified into groups based on the different ways their structures develop.

I. Using a scalpel or knife, dissect the examples of fruits found in the lab. (Your teacher may assign a different fruit to each laboratory group to dissect, or the fruits may already be dissected for you.)

II. Use the Key to Common Fruit Types (p. 125) to identify the type of each of the fruit specimens.

Fruit Types

Specimen	Name of Fruit	Fruit Type	Specimen	Name of Fruit	Fruit Type
A			G		
B			H		
C			I		
D			J		
E			K		
F			L		

B

III. In Area B draw longitudinal section views of the fruits your teacher selects and label the parts indicated by the fruit type. Research may be necessary.

- Pome: Label receptacle, ovary, remains of flower parts, pedicel, ovary wall, and seeds.
- Drupe: Label pedicel, remains of flower parts, ovary (outer layer and inner layer), and seed.
- True berry: Label pedicel, remains of flower parts, skin, ovary, section of fruit, and seeds.
- Pod: Label pedicel, remains of flower parts, ovary, and seeds.
- Modified berry: Label pedicel, remains of flower parts, skin, ovary, section of fruit, and seeds.

A Key to Common Fruit Types

1. Single ovary that may have one or more chambers for ovules, usually without other floral parts .... (simple fruit) **3**

   Collection of ovaries, usually with other floral parts .... (compound fruit) **2**

Compound fruits

2. Several separate ovaries of a single flower that ripen individually, usually on an enlarged receptacle .... **aggregate fruit**

   Several ovaries from separate flowers that ripen fused together, usually on an enlarged receptacle .... **multiple fruit**

Simple fruits

3. Fruit dry at maturity .... (dry fruit) **4**

   Fruit fleshy at maturity .... (fleshy fruit) **10**

Dry simple fruits

4. Fruit open when ripe **5**

   Fruit closed when ripe **7**

5. Ovary wall thin. Single-chambered ovary with many seeds. Opens along one or two sides when ripe **6**

   Ovary wall thin. Multiple-chambered ovary, each chamber with many seeds. Opens when ripe .... **capsule**

6. Opens along one side .... **follicle**

   Opens along two sides .... **pod**

7. Fruit with thin wing formed by ovary wall .... **samara**

   Fruit without wing **8**

8. Thick, hard, woody ovary wall enclosing a single seed .... **nut**

   Thin ovary wall **9**

9. Ovary wall fastened to a single seed .... **grain**

   Ovary wall separated from a single seed .... **achene**

Fleshy simple fruits

10. Fleshy portion develops from receptacle enlargement. Ovary forms leathery core with seeds .... **pome**

    Ovary fleshy **11**

11. Ovary two-layered, outer layer fleshy and inner layer forming hard woody stone or pit, usually enclosing one seed .... **drupe**

    Entire ovary fleshy **12**

12. Thin-skinned fruit with divided ovary, usually with each section containing seeds .... **true berry**

    Thick, tough-skinned, with divided ovary, usually with each section containing seeds .... **modified berry**

Seeds

The three basic parts of a seed are the embryo plant, stored food, and a seed coat. The diversity of these structures found in different plants, however, is almost as wide as the diversity found in the floral parts and fruit types.

I. Observe the seed(s) found in the lab. (Your teacher may assign a different seed to each laboratory group or may give each group a few seeds to observe and dissect.)

- Use a hand lens to observe the exterior structures of the seed(s).

- Seek to identify the following structures:
  - The *hilum* (point where the seed was attached to the ovary)
  - The *micropyle* (point where the pollen tube entered the ovule)

- In Area C draw the seed you observed, labeling as many parts as you can.

II. Dissect the seed(s) supplied by your instructor.

- You will need to use a sharp scalpel or a single-edged razor blade to dissect most seeds.
  - If your dissection instrument is dull, you will damage the structures.
  - The size or hardness of some seeds makes using a sharp instrument dangerous.
    - If possible, hold the seed with forceps or other instruments, not your fingers, when you are attempting to cut it open.
    - If your seed is very hard (a nut or a pit), you may need to use special instruments to open it. Your teacher will give you special instructions.

- Often a single, well-placed cut will reveal all of the structures listed below. Some seeds, however, will require additional cuts. Some seeds (like nuts) must be taken apart in pieces to reveal all of the structures.

- Once you have dissected the seed, seek to find the following parts:
  - The embryo plant, composed of the epicotyl, hypocotyl, and radicle
  - The cotyledon(s)
  - The endosperm

- Is the seed you dissected a monocot or a dicot?   ☐ monocot   ☐ dicot

- In Area D draw the seed you dissected, labeling as many parts as you can.
  - You may need to draw both halves of your dissected seed to get all the parts in your drawing.
  - You may need to reconstruct some of your dissected seed in order to draw it.

- After everyone is finished, observe each other's dissected seeds and drawings.

C

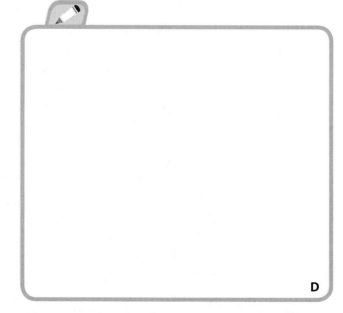

D

15a Porifera

Introduction

You will study these unusual animals in phylum Porifera by observing preserved specimens. Before you begin, read carefully the Life Processes Chart for *Grantia*. You are responsible for knowing the structures and functions of each organism covered in the laboratory exercises as an example of the particular phylum you are studying.

Goals

✓ Observe typical sponges

✓ Draw some conclusions regarding the structure and unique characteristics of sponges

Grantia

I.   Study the picture of *Grantia* in your text on page 345.

II. Without using the microscope, observe a cross section and a longitudinal section of *Grantia* found on a preserved slide. Measure the height and width of these sections of *Grantia*: _____ mm high by _____ mm wide.

III. Scan both the c.s. and the l.s. of a *Grantia* preserved slide under a microscope.

- How is the sponge structure of *Grantia* classified?
  ☐ simple   ☐ complex

  Why?

  _____

  _____

- After studying your text and a preserved slide prepared for observing spicules, describe the spicules of a *Grantia*.

  _____

  _____

  _____

  _____

Materials

preserved slides of *Grantia*, c.s. and l.s., and *Grantia* spicules

preserved specimens of various sponges

dissection kit

hand lens

microscope

glass slides

cover slips

IV. Draw a portion of a *Grantia* cross section in Area A by following these directions:

- Include sections of both cell layers and the mesenchyme.

- Label as many different structures as you can see.

- Poriferans are classified as animals instead of plants. Based on observations of their cells, what proof can you give to support this?

  _____

  _____

Bath Sponge

I.   Observe a preserved specimen of a bath sponge.

- What structures are you able to see?

  _____

A

- Classify the structure of a bath sponge: ☐simple ☐complex

  Why?

  _____

- Often the structure of an organism will determine how a certain function is carried out. In the sponge, how does the structure affect the function of obtaining food?

  _____

  _____

  _____

II. Observe the spongin network of a bath sponge.
- Use a hand lens to observe the spongin fiber network of a bath sponge.
  - ☐ Observe sections of a dry bath sponge and of a wet bath sponge.
  - ☐ What differences are you able to observe?

    _____

    _____

- Make a wet mount of the spongin fibers of a bath sponge.
  - ☐ Use a very small piece of sponge.
  - ☐ Describe what you see.

    _____

    _____

  - ☐ Draw in Area B several of the spongin fibers as seen on low power of your microscope.
- If you were given an unknown sample, what characteristics could you use to classify the organism in the phylum Porifera?

  _____

  _____

  _____

B

Life Processes Charts

The nine basic life processes that all animals accomplish are described on pages 341–42 of your text. As you read about and study the various animal phyla, you will learn about the methods and structures they use to accomplish these life functions. To help you associate the different organisms with their structures and methods and to make sure that you have grasped all the information you need to know, you will fill in Life Processes Charts for the representative animals of several phyla.

Unless you are told otherwise, you will find in your text most of the information you need to fill in these charts. When you finish them, they will serve as excellent study guides as well as reveal how carefully you have read.

On pages 129–30, a Life Processes Chart has been completed for the sponge *Grantia*. Because *Grantia* is a simple organism, not all the spaces on the chart have been used. The entry in the Notes column describes, defines, or explains the entry in the Structure column. The lack of special structures for a particular function *does not* indicate that an organism does not accomplish that function. You should explain in the Notes column the way it accomplishes that function. Normally, the first time you use a term in a Life Processes Chart, you should define it in the Notes column.

Life Processes Chart

Organism _____ Sponge (*Grantia*) _____

Phylum _____ Porifera _____ **Class** _____ —— _____ **Genus** _____ *Grantia* _____

Structure   **Notes**

Movement *(structures responsible for movement; types of movement)*

No structures   Sessile; it moves its environment (water) into ostia and out the osculum. (See *Collar cells* under Nutrition below.)

_____

_____

_____

_____

Body Covering *(what covers the body; how it protects the animal)*

Epidermis   One cell layer thick. (Some sponges, like *Grantia*, have spicules that stick through the epidermis for protection.)

_____

_____

_____

_____

Support *(structures responsible for support; what they are made of)*

Spicules   Made of lime; help to support. (NOTE: Spicules of other sponges are made of silica and spongin.)

            Much support comes from fullness caused by mesenchyme filling between cell layers.

_____

_____

_____

Nutrition *(structures of digestion; methods of ingestion; types of food; assimilation)*

Collar cells   Food is carried in by currents made by collar cells, engulfed by collar cells, and digested in vacuoles of the collar cells.

            Nondigestible material is egested.

            Food: algae, protozoans, bacteria, etc.

_____

_____

Respiration *(structures used in gas exchange for respiration)*

No structures   Gases are exchanged by diffusion between cells and water environment.

_____

_____

_____

_____

Structure	Notes
Circulation (structures responsible for internal movement of substances)	
Amoebocytes	Cells in the mesenchyme; in larger sponges these cells transport substances.
	Most circulation takes place by diffusion.
Excretion (structures for the collection and elimination of soluble wastes)	
No structures	Wastes are released by diffusion.
Responses (structures for receiving stimuli and for responses; level of responses)	
No structures	Osculum sometimes can be closed in response to substances in water.
	Collar cells can change their rate of flagellar movement.
Reproduction—Asexual (structures for and types of asexual reproduction)	
Gemmules	Some freshwater sponges produce gemmules to survive unfavorable conditions.
Budding	Most sponges reproduce by buds and regenerate by fragmentation.
Reproduction—Sexual (structures for sexual reproduction)	
Testes	Eggs and sperm are produced by one sponge or by separate sponges.
Ovaries	

Other Notes (habitat, size, range, unusual examples, etc.)

Most are marine; some, freshwater.

Many are small; a few, large.

Simple sponges usually have only one cavity; complex sponges may have thick walls and many cavities.

Bath sponges have a spongin network of fibers.

They are either asymmetrical or radially symmetrical.

15b Cnidaria

Introduction

Although many widely varying animals belong in the phylum Cnidaria, they all have body forms and responses similar to the hydra. Therefore, you will study the hydra in detail as a representative cnidarian and then observe other examples.

Class Hydrozoa: The Hydra

R E O

I. Study the life processes of the hydra and prepare a Life Processes Chart for the hydra.

II. Draw the hydra.

R E O

- In Area A, make an *outline* drawing of an entire hydra with bud from a preserved slide. Use only low power.

  □ The entire hydra will not fit into the microscope field. You will need to move the slide several times as you draw.

  □ Label the mouth, the tentacles, and any buds that you see.

R E O

- Using high power, draw a portion of the hydra body wall, c.s., in Area B.

  □ This drawing should include *internal structures*, not just be an outline.

  □ Label as many of the cellular structures of the hydra as you can.

Materials

preserved slides of a plain hydra and budding hydra, a cross section of a hydra, a hydra with ovaries, and a hydra with testes

preserved specimens of coral and jellyfish

living cultures of hydras and brine shrimp or *Daphnia*

spring water

dissection kit

hand lens

microscope

dilute acetic acid (vinegar)

culture dishes

pipet

glass slides

concavity slides

cover slips

A

B

C

- In Area C, using low power, prepare an outline drawing of an entire hydra with ovaries and testes. Label the ovaries and testes.

III. Observe a living hydra.

- To obtain a living hydra for observation, do the following:
  - Fill a clean culture dish with spring water (or treated, "aged," or pond water).
  - Using a pipet, follow these instructions to obtain a specimen from the culture.
    - Flush a stream of water from the pipet onto the hydra you have selected in order to dislodge the specimen.
    - Draw the dislodged hydra into your pipet and flush it onto the culture dish.

- Observe your living hydra and the hydras of other students in your class during the class period. Identify as many different forms of locomotion or movement as you can. Describe as many forms as you observe.

_____

_____

_____

_____

- Study the nerves and the responses of the hydra.
  - The hydra's nervous system consists of a nerve net. From the information in your text (and possibly other research), describe a nerve net.

  _____

  _____

  - Observe the responses of the hydra.
    - Very gently swirl the water around the hydra. What is its reaction?

    _____

♦ After the hydra has recovered from the above experiment (which may take several minutes), touch your probe as gently as possible to its base. What is its reaction?

_____

♦ After the hydra has recovered from the above experiment, touch your probe as gently as possible to one of its tentacles. What is its reaction?

_____

♦ After the hydra has recovered from the above experiment, arrange your probe so that the hydra may touch the probe of its own power. What is its reaction?

_____

• Observe the feeding process of the hydra.

  □ Using a pipet, place a few living *Daphnia* or brine shrimp in your culture dish near the hydra. Be careful not to add the food so rapidly that you disturb the hydra. Do not try to force-feed the hydra but keep the food within tentacle reach.

  □ Using a hand lens, watch carefully the actions of your hydra. Note especially any activity in the mouth region.

  □ From your observations, describe the feeding process of the hydra.

  _____

  _____

  □ Describe digestion in a hydra by answering the following questions.

    ♦ In what structure of the hydra does extracellular digestion take place?

    _____

    ♦ What cells provide the enzymes for this digestion?

    _____

    ♦ What happens to the partially digested food?

    _____

    ♦ What happens to the substances that cannot be digested?

    _____

• Typical food for a hydra includes

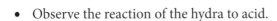

• Observe the reaction of the hydra to acid.

  □ Carefully remove your hydra and set it in a large drop of spring water placed on a concavity slide.

  □ Place a cover slip over the slide and observe the hydra (or sections of it) with a microscope.

  □ After it has recovered from the transfer and you have been able to focus on cells of its tentacles, place a small drop of the dilute acetic acid on the edge of the cover slip.

  □ Watch the hydra carefully. For the best results, one partner should put the acetic acid on the slide while the other partner observes the reaction through the microscope.

  □ What did you observe as the acid reached the hydra?

  _____

R E O

- Draw conclusions from your observations of the movement, feeding, and reactions of the hydra.
  - Is the hydra able to respond differently to various stimuli? ☐ yes ☐ no
  - What reaction(s) did you observe?

    _____

    _____

  - Why are the reactions of the hydra limited?

    _____

    _____

  - Compare the ways sponges and hydras get food based on their structure.

    _____

    _____

    _____

    _____

- To remove your hydra, flush the slide with spring water while holding it over a separate culture container for "used" hydras. Do not return the hydra to its original culture.

Class Anthozoa: The Coral

R E O

I. Observe the preserved coral specimens in the classroom. What structure are you actually observing?

_____

II. Compare a living coral organism and a hydra.

_____

_____

Class Scyphozoa: The Jellyfish

R E O

I. Observe and describe the preserved jellyfish in the classroom.

_____

II. Compare a jellyfish and a hydra (diagrams may be helpful).

_____

_____

_____

name: _____

section: _____ date: _____

15c Worms I: Platyhelminthes and Nematoda

Introduction

In this laboratory exercise you will observe free-living and parasitic flat-worms (phylum Platyhelminthes) and some significant roundworms (phylum Nematoda). Although Annelida may be the most familiar of the worm phyla, these two phyla contain organisms that are far more significant to humans because of the diseases they cause.

Platyhelminthes

Phylum Platyhelminthes contains simple organisms with only three basic cell layers: an epidermis, a gastroderm, and a mesoderm. Various structures develop from these cell layers. Some of these structures correspond to many of the organs and systems in more complex animals. The flatworms exhibit two lifestyles: free-living and parasitic. We will examine the planarian as an example of the free-living variety.

Free-Living Flatworms: The Planarian

I. Read the sections in your text that deal with phylum Platyhelminthes (pp. 351–56), and then prepare a Life Processes Chart for the planarian.

Laboratory Techniques for Handling Planarians

- Fill a clean culture dish with fresh spring water.
- Move the planarian by following these instructions:
  □ Agitate the water around the planarian (make small currents with a pipet) until it floats around in the water.
  □ Quickly draw it into the pipet.
  □ Quickly put it into the container you have ready. Speed is important; if the planarian uncoils and attaches itself to the inside of the pipet, it is often difficult to remove.
- On occasion it will be best to put your planarian on a glass slide in order to restrain it and to view its ventral surface easily. If you use a concavity slide, a cover slip can be placed on it. However, if you use a flat slide, the cover slip will squash the planarian.

II. Observe the movement of planarians.

- Obtain a planarian by following the instructions in the box.
- Study the two different means by which the planarians move.
  □ Ciliary movement
    ♦ Where are the cilia located on the planarian?

_____

Goals

✓ Observe planarians and other flatworms

✓ Draw conclusions about the structure and special characteristics of flatworms

✓ Compare planarians and various flatworms to previously studied organisms

✓ Recognize some of the more familiar nematodes that can infect humans

Materials

culture of living planarians

spring water

culture dish

dissection kit

hand lens

Epsom salts

concavity slides

preserved slides of beef tapeworm (*Taenia saginata*) scolex, proglottid, and bladders in meat

preserved specimens or preserved slides of *Ascaris lumbricoides*, *Clonorchis sinensis*, *Necator americanus*, and *Trichinella spiralis*

illuminator (optional)

microscope

♦ After observing the planarian moving by using its cilia, describe this type of movement.

_____

   □ Muscular movement
   ♦ Place a few grains of Epsom salts into the water right next to the planarian. Watch carefully as the Epsom salts begin to dissolve near it.
   ♦ After you have observed the movement that results, remove and discard the grains of salt and add some fresh spring water to dilute the salt.
   ♦ Describe muscular movement in comparison to the ciliary movement you have described above.

_____

_____

   ♦ Where are the structures for muscular movement located?

_____

• Briefly compare the structures for movement in the planarian to structures for movement in the hydra.

_____

_____

III. Observe the responses of planarians.
   • Observe the responses to touch.
   □ With a clean probe, touch very lightly the lateral surface of the planarian. What is the response?

_____

   □ Touch lightly an auricle (side point of the head). What is the response?

_____

   □ Touch lightly the posterior end. What is the response?

_____

   • Observe the responses to current.
   □ Fill a clean pipet with water and slowly force the water out to produce a current.
   □ Direct the current to one side of the planarian in the culture dish. (Take about thirty seconds to empty one pipet of water. Have several pipets ready.) What is its response?

_____

   □ Direct a current toward the side of the planarian's head. What is its response?

_____

   □ Direct a current toward the posterior end, directly behind the planarian. What is its response?

_____

   • Compare the degree of specialization (how specific the responses are) in the planarian and in the hydra.

_____

_____

IV. Investigate the ingestion and digestion of planarians.
   • Place your planarian on a glass slide, using the techniques described in the box (p. 135).
   • Look for the structures the planarian uses to get food.
   □ Holding the slide above your head, look for the mouth and pharynx of your planarian.

        ▫ Describe the mouth's location on the body.

_____

        ▫ Describe the appearance and the function of the pharynx.

_____

- Describe the digestion of planarians.

        ▫ Describe the area within the planarian where digestion begins. Be sure to use the proper name for this structure.

_____

_____

        ▫ After the structure described above completes preliminary digestion, what happens to the small particles of food to complete digestion?

_____

_____

Parasitic Flatworms

There are many different types of parasitic platyhelminths. You will study two of the most common human parasites: the beef tapeworm (*Taenia saginata*) and the human liver fluke (*Clonorchis sinensis*). These two pathogenic organisms are examples of different classes in the phylum Platyhelminthes.

I. Study the beef tapeworm.

- Using low power, observe preserved slides of the following stages (structures) in the life cycle of the beef tapeworm: scolex, mature proglottid, and bladders in meat.
- Study the life cycle of the beef tapeworm.
    - ▫ Carefully study the outline of the beef tapeworm's life cycle given below.
    - ▫ From your observations, complete Figure 15c-1, which shows the beef tapeworm's life cycle stages.
    - ▫ Add labeled drawings in the three circles of the figure.
    - ▫ Add the following labels in the places they belong: intestine of man, intestine of cow, blood vessel of cow, contaminated meat, adult tapeworm, egg containing six-hooked larva.

Life Cycle of a Beef Tapeworm

- Eggs of the tapeworm are eaten by the cow.
    - ▫ Eggs hatch in the intestine as a six-hooked larva.
    - ▫ The larva bores through the intestinal wall, enters the bloodstream, and is carried to a muscle.
- The larva burrows into the muscle.
    - ▫ In the muscle, the larva becomes a bladder worm (cyst).
    - ▫ Inside the bladder is an immature scolex.
- The muscle infected with the bladder worm is eaten by a human.
    - ▫ If the meat is not cooked enough or treated to kill the bladder worm, the bladder worm hatches in the human's intestine.
    - ▫ The scolex (head) of the tapeworm embeds itself in the lining of the intestine.
- The adult tapeworm lives in the intestine of a human.
    - ▫ The scolex produces proglottids (the chain of which may be over ten feet in length), which contain hundreds of eggs.
    - ▫ The ripe proglottids are passed in the feces.
    - ▫ Cows graze on grass fertilized with infected feces.

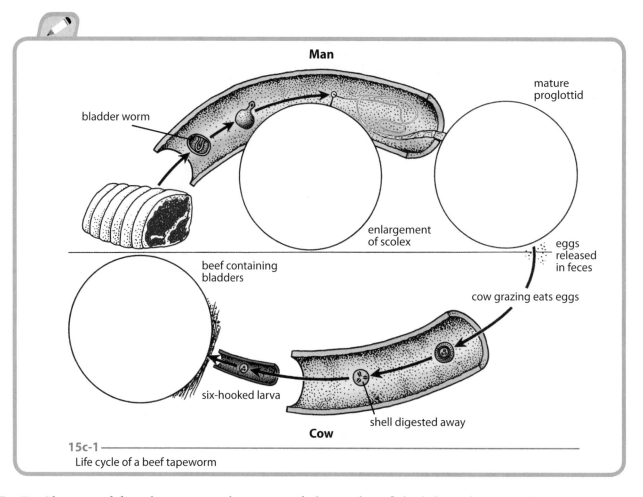

Man

mature
proglottid

bladder worm

enlargement
of scolex

eggs
released
in feces

beef containing
bladders

cow grazing eats eggs

six-hooked larva

shell digested away

Cow

15c-1
Life cycle of a beef tapeworm

II. Observe and describe a preserved specimen of a human liver fluke (*Clonorchis sinensis*).

_____

_____

Nematoda: Roundworms

The roundworms (phylum Nematoda) are surprisingly alike in their body structure but are extremely diverse in their habitats and life cycles. In this section you will observe some of the organisms that are pathogenic to humans.

I. Prepare a Life Processes Chart for *Ascaris*.

II. Observe preserved specimens or slides of various roundworms and describe them (color, length, shape, etc.).

- Human *Ascaris* (*Ascaris lumbricoides*)

  _____

  _____

- Hookworms (*Necator americanus*)

  _____

  _____

- Trichina worms (*Trichinella spiralis*)

  _____

  _____

15d Worms II: Annelida

name: _____

section: _____ date: _____

Introduction

The organisms in phylum Annelida are very diverse. For classroom observation the most common of the annelids, the earthworm, is an excellent choice, even though it may not be considered typical of all the organisms in this phylum.

In this laboratory exercise you will be asked to dissect an earthworm. This is the first laboratory dissection you are asked to do for this course. To prepare for it, be sure you read the information in the Dissection Techniques box and define the terms indicated. These terms will be commonly used in describing dissection procedures.

Dissection Techniques

General Instructions
These instructions apply to all dissections in this laboratory manual.
- Read carefully the entire exercise before you begin. This reading can prevent many wrong cuts.
- Reread the directions before you begin to cut.
- Make sure you have identified the correct structures by comparing them to drawings before you cut.
- Handle the specimens delicately. Preserved structures often tear and break easily.

Temporarily Storing a Dissection Animal
- Put your name and lab hour on a plastic bag with a permanent marker.
- Wrap the organism in a very wet paper towel.
- Place the organism and the wet paper towel in the plastic bag. Gently squeeze out most of the air and tie or zip the bag closed.
- Organisms wrapped in this manner may be kept for a few days without great deterioration.

Dissection Vocabulary
Define the following terms. Be sure you know how they apply to each animal before you begin a dissection. **The terms *right* and *left* in the instructions refer to the organism's right and left, not yours.**
- Anterior: _____
- Posterior: _____
- Dorsal: _____
- Ventral: _____
- Median: _____
- Longitudinal: _____
- Transverse: _____
- Lateral: _____
- Cephalic: _____
- Caudal: _____

Goals
✓ Introduce dissection techniques
✓ Observe the structures of an earthworm
✓ Compare the earthworm to other organisms

Materials
dissection kit
hand lens
flashlight or illuminator
living earthworms
preserved earthworms
dissection pan
dissection pins
plastic bag
ether
alcohol

Earthworm Dissection

External Structures

I. Examine your specimen carefully.

- Rub your fingers lightly across its surface.
- As you touch the skin of the earthworm, you should feel tiny bristles.
  - What are these bristles called?

  _____

  - How many are there on each segment?

  _____

  - On what area of the body do these bristles appear?

  _____

  - How do they help in locomotion?

  _____

II. Does the earthworm have definite anterior and posterior ends that can be determined by sight? ☐ yes ☐ no
Explain your answer.

_____

- Locate the prostomium. What is its function?

_____

- Locate the anus. What is its function?

_____

III. Examine the clitellum.

- How many segments are there in the clitellum? _____
- What is the function of the clitellum?

_____

IV. Examine other body openings.

- Using a hand lens, try to locate the nephridiopores. How many are there on each segment? _____
- Examine segment 14 and locate the female pore through which eggs leave the body. (NOTE: Segments are numbered beginning at the mouth and continuing toward the anus.)
- Locate the male pore in segment 15. Sperm leave the body through this opening.
- Try to locate the openings in the furrows between segments 9 and 10 and segments 10 and 11 through which sperm enter the body. (These are sometimes impossible to locate.)

Opening the Body Cavity

I. Place your specimen in a dissection pan with the dorsal side up.

II. Pin the anterior and posterior ends to the pan, using care not to put the pins through any internal organs.

III. Place your scissors slightly to the left of the mid dorsal line and about an inch posterior to the clitellum. Carefully cut through the body wall. Then extend the cut anteriorly to the prostomium. *Be careful not to cut anything but the body wall.*

IV. Separate the edges of the cut and look into the body cavity.

- Observe that the body wall is separated from the intestine by a space. What is this space called?

  _____

- Notice that the space is divided by partitions extending from the body wall to the intestine. What are these partitions called?

  _____

- Using forceps and probes, carefully break these partitions segment by segment until the internal structures found in the anterior end of the worm are entirely exposed for study.
- To hold the body wall open, pin it to the wax or pad in the dissection pan.

Locating the Earthworm's Muscular Structures

I. Locate the circular and longitudinal muscles in one or two of the segments of your worm. (This is sometimes difficult with small preserved worms.)

II. Suppose that the worm's circular muscles have already contracted and its setae have anchored its anterior end to the soil. In the earthworm's movements, what structures will function next and what movement will result?

_____

Locating the Earthworm's Interior Digestive Structures

I. Locate the pharynx, a thick-walled area posterior to the buccal cavity. What is the purpose of the thick walls?

_____

II. Locate the esophagus, which extends from the pharynx to segment 14. What is the function of the esophagus?

_____

III. Locate the crop, a large, thin-walled area posterior to the esophagus. What is the function of this structure?

_____

IV. Locate the gizzard, a thick-walled area posterior to the crop. What is the function of the gizzard?

_____

V. Locate the intestine, which extends from the gizzard to the anus. What is the function of the intestine?

_____

VI. Make an outline drawing of the digestive system in the earthworm outline provided in Figure 15d-1. Be sure to include all the structures listed in the digestive section (above), and be sure they are in the correct body segments.

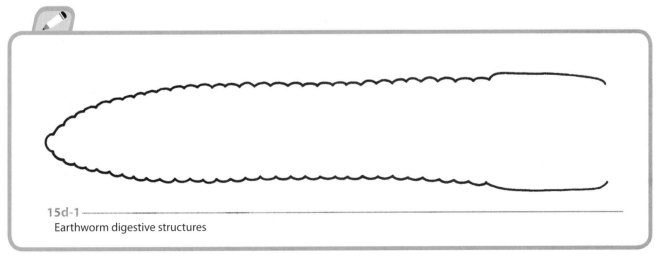

15d-1
Earthworm digestive structures

Locating the Earthworm's Circulatory Structures

I. Find the dorsal blood vessel on your specimen. It appears as a dark, brownish-colored vessel running along the medial surface of the intestine. In many specimens you can see this structure lying on the intestine.

II. Remove the seminal vesicles by lifting them out from the left side of the body.

III. Look in segment 11 for a pair of stout tubes coming from the dorsal blood vessel and extending ventrally. These "hearts," or aortic arches, are often discolored because they contain blood. What is the function of these structures?

_____

IV. Look at each segment from 7 to 11 for the rest of the aortic arches. You will have to remove the septa to see these clearly.

V. Near the posterior section of your cut, use probes to move the intestine to the right and try to find the ventral blood vessel. (This structure is often difficult to locate.) Does it look any different from the dorsal blood vessel? ☐ yes ☐ no

VI. Make an outline drawing of the circulatory system in the earthworm outline provided in Figure 15d-2.

- Include and label the dorsal blood vessels, the ventral blood vessels, and the aortic arches. Be sure they are in the correct segment.

- Make the drawing as though it were being viewed laterally.

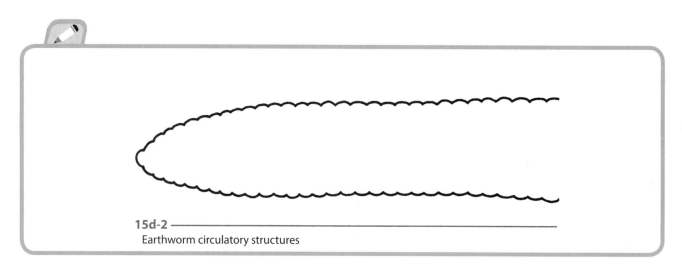

15d-2 ——————————————————
Earthworm circulatory structures

Locating the Earthworm's Excretory Structures

I. Nephridia are located in every segment except for the first three and the last one.

- Extend the body wall incision posteriorly about two inches.
- Carefully open the body wall in this area, trying not to tear the septa.
- Carefully remove the intestine from the area.
- Use a hand lens or stereomicroscope to find the nephridia. (In some specimens the nephridia are difficult to find.)

II. To what human organ do the nephridia of the earthworm correspond? _____

Locating the Earthworm's Nervous System

Locating these structures may be difficult, and if you have not been careful in your dissecting, you may have destroyed them. A hand lens may be helpful.

I. In the area of segments 2 and 3, dorsal to the buccal cavity, the "brain," or suprapharyngeal (*supra* "above," and *pharyngeal* "pharynx") ganglia, is located. Try to find the suprapharyngeal ganglia.

II. Two nerve fibers extend from the suprapharyngeal ganglia, pass around the pharynx, and join below the pharynx at the subpharyngeal (*sub* "below") ganglion. Try to locate the subpharyngeal ganglion.

III. The ventral nerve cord extends from the subpharyngeal ganglion. Remove a part of the intestine from the posterior part of the body and try to locate the nerve cord.

IV. Note the small ganglion present in each segment. Also note the small nerves going from each of these ganglia into the body wall.

V. In Figure 15d-3, label the suprapharyngeal ganglia, subpharyngeal ganglion, ventral nerve cord, nerve cord ganglia, and nerves to body segments.

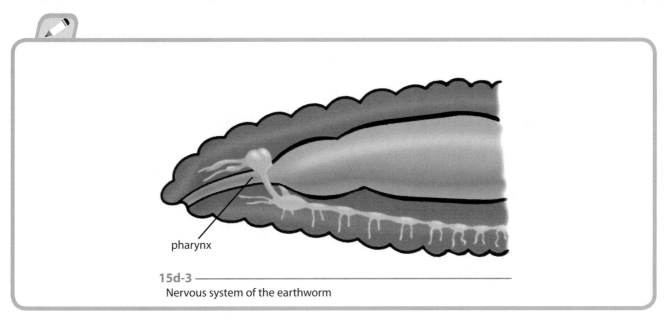

pharynx

15d-3 ——————————————————
Nervous system of the earthworm

Locating the Earthworm's Reproductive Structures

I. The parts of the reproductive system are found in the first fifteen segments.

II. Segments 9 to 13 contain pairs of white structures called seminal vesicles. Sperm are stored in these organs.

III. Segments 9 and 10 contain pairs of small, white, spherical structures called seminal receptacles. These organs receive sperm from other earthworms.

IV. Locate the small ovaries, in which the eggs develop. They are under the seminal vesicles.

Testing Reactions of a Live Earthworm

To see how an earthworm responds to various stimuli, you will need to test a living earthworm. Place a living specimen in a clean dissection pan that has a number of crumpled, wet paper towels in it. Keep the earthworm wet. After you have finished the experiments, return the worm to the laboratory culture.

Testing the Earthworm's Response to Touch

I. Touch the posterior end lightly with a probe. (Do not stab it.)

- Pause until the earthworm is moving slowly.

- Repeat several times.

- What is the worm's reaction?

II. Do the same to the anterior end. What is its reaction?

_____

III. As the worm lies on the paper towels, touch its body near the middle as low on its side as you can. What is the reaction?

_____

Testing the Earthworm's Response to Light

R E O

I. Remove the towels from the dissection pan, cover the pan, and keep the worm in the dark for several minutes.

II. Peek inside (keeping it as dark as possible) to find the worm's anterior end.

III. Still keeping conditions as dark as possible, shine the flashlight or illuminator on the worm's anterior end. What is its reaction?

_____

Dissection of a Live Earthworm

R E O

Under supervision, two students will anesthetize a live earthworm with ether and follow the directions given earlier for opening the body cavity. All students will observe the specimen and then answer the following questions. After the class's observation, the worm will be put to death with alcohol.

I. What moving structures indicate that the earthworm is alive?

_____

II. How do the aortic arches beat? ☐ in unison ☐ in a rhythm ☐ without coordination

III. Other than movement, what are the major differences between the preserved specimen and the live specimen? Can you explain these differences?

_____

_____

_____

16a   Crustaceans

Introduction

You will begin this laboratory exercise by studying crayfish appendages, noting their varied shapes and functions, and then studying the life processes of a crayfish. As you observe other crustaceans or other arthropods, you will find that although their structures vary greatly, the basic body plan is the same in all of them.

External Anatomy of the Crayfish

The Segments of the Exoskeleton

I. Place your crayfish in a dissection pan and carefully observe the dorsal side of your specimen.

- As you find each of the structures italicized below, label them on Figure 16a-1. NOTE: You may need to draw in details in order to label all the structures.

- Examine the hard, chitinous *exoskeleton* covering the crayfish and note that the body is divided into two main regions, the *cephalothorax* and the *abdomen*.

II. Examine the cephalothorax, the anterior region of the crayfish.

- Note that the cephalothorax is covered by a single piece of exoskeleton called the *carapace*.

  □ The anterior extension of the carapace, which forms a horny beak between the eyes of the crayfish, is called the *rostrum*.

  □ Locate the *cervical groove* on the carapace, which marks the division between the *head* and the *thorax*.

- Note the segments of the cephalothorax.

  □ There are either thirteen or fourteen segments in the cephalothorax, depending on whether the segment preceding the one bearing the antennules is considered a true segment.

  □ On the ventral side these segments are easy to locate if you remember that there is one set of appendages per segment.

III. Examine the abdomen of the crayfish.

- How many segments (not appendages) are there in the abdomen? _____

- The last segment is called the *telson*. Label it on Figure 16a-1.

- Although it is not a segment, locate the anal opening on the ventral side of the abdomen.

The Appendages of the Head

If possible, continue to label Figure 16a-1 with the italicized structures discussed in this section.

I. Locate the appendages of sensation.

- What is an appendage?

  _____

- Although they do not fit the definition of a true appendage, locate the stalked *compound eyes*.

Goals

✓ Observe arthropod characteristics in the crayfish

✓ Note the variety of appendages and the specialization of internal parts of a crayfish

✓ Observe other crustaceans and compare them to the crayfish

Materials

preserved crayfish

dissection kit

dissection pan

culture dish

preserved specimens showing crayfish life cycle

preserved specimens of other crustaceans

plastic bag

microscope

preserved slides of crustaceans

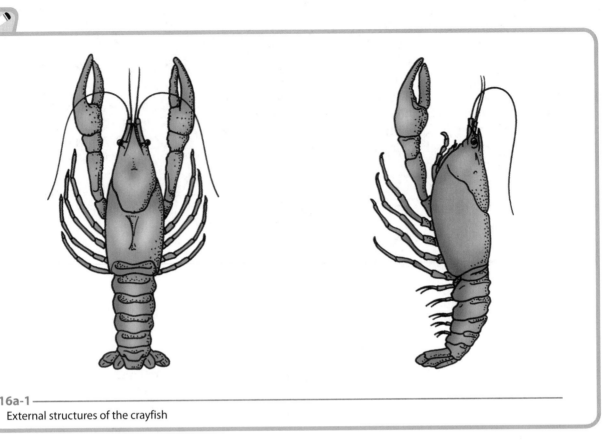

16a-1
External structures of the crayfish

- Locate the most anterior appendages, the *antennules*.
  - ▫ How many antennules are there? _____
  - ▫ They are used for balance, taste, and touch.
- Other appendages near the antennules are the long *antennae*.
  - ▫ How many of these are there? _____
  - ▫ They are used for taste and touch.

II. Locate the appendages of the mouth.
- Turn your crayfish ventral side up in the dissection pan and locate all the mouthparts.
- Compare what you find with those drawn in Figure 16a-2.
- Do not remove them.
  - ▫ The one pair of mandibles (or true jaws) is just posterior to the antennae. They are small, hard coverings of the mouth that pulverize food.
  - ▫ The two pairs of maxillae are just posterior to the mandibles and assist in chewing.
  - ▫ The three pairs of *maxillipeds* (or jaw feet) are posterior to the maxillae. (When counting these appendages, do not be fooled by their branched appearance.) Maxillipeds are used to hold food in place.
- Observe mouthpart movement.
  - ▫ Human mouthparts move vertically (up and down). In what direction do the mouthparts of a crayfish move? (Note especially the mandibles.)

    _____

  - ▫ Does this characteristic reinforce the idea that the mouthparts are appendages?   ☐ yes   ☐ no

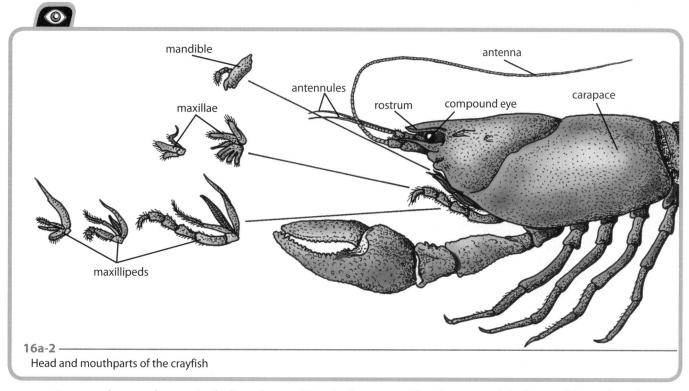

16a-2
Head and mouthparts of the crayfish

- Remove the mouthparts, including the maxillipeds, from one side of your crayfish. (You still have the other side of the organism to work with if you are unsuccessful the first time.)
  - ▫ Remove the maxillipeds; then locate and remove the other mouthparts.
  - ▫ To remove the appendage, grip the base with forceps and pull the entire appendage out.
- Draw in Area A all the mouth appendages you have removed from the crayfish.
  - ▫ Label the drawing completely.
  - ▫ Draw the appendages in the order they were in the crayfish, the most anterior at the left of the drawing and the most posterior at the right.

The Appendages of the Thorax

As you locate each of the appendages discussed and italicized below, label them on Figure 16a-1.

I. The thoracic appendages move either the organism or the materials around the organism.

How many pairs of appendages does the thorax have? _____

A

II. The most obvious appendages of the thorax are the *chelipeds*. Note the large pincers (the claws), which are used for protection and capturing food.

III. The next four pairs of appendages are *walking legs*. Carefully examine these thoracic appendages. How do these legs differ from one another?

_____

Do all the walking legs have pincers? If not, which do?

_____

The Appendages of the Abdomen

I. The abdomen has five pairs of appendages called *swimmerets*. Label these on Figure 16a-1.

II. Carefully examine preserved male and female crayfish.

- In the male, the most anterior swimmerets are enlarged and point anteriorly. In the female, the anterior swimmerets are greatly reduced in size.
- What sex is your crayfish? ☐ male ☐ female

III. The sixth abdominal appendages are called the *uropods*. They grow from the telson.

Together these structures form a powerful tail fin. How would the crayfish use these?

_____

Internal Anatomy of the Crayfish

Read all the following directions carefully before starting your dissection. The following procedures must be done in order. You will be expected to know the functions and locations of the organs that have been italicized.

The Body Cavity

I. Place your animal in the dissection pan with its dorsal side up.

II. Carefully insert the point of the scissors under the dorsal surface of the carapace at the posterior edge of the cephalothorax. Cut anteriorly along the midline of the body to the rostrum.

III. Reposition the scissors just behind the eyes and make a transverse cut.

IV. Carefully remove the two pieces of the carapace without disturbing the structures underneath.

The Respiratory Structures

I. Note carefully the exposed gills and study their structure.

- Remove a few gills and place them in a culture dish of water. Observe and describe their structure.

_____

- Carefully remove the rest of the gills.

II. Gills are able to exchange gases only when they are wet. Explain how the crayfish can spend many hours at a time on land.

_____

_____

The Circulatory Structures

I. For easier handling of the animal, remove the legs attached to the thorax.

II. Carefully separate the dorsal tissues in the thorax and locate the mid dorsal *heart*.

- Locate the main *blood vessels* attached to the heart.

- The crayfish, as well as most other arthropods, has an open circulatory system.
  - How does an open circulatory system work?

  _____

  - Does an open circulatory system circulate materials as efficiently as a closed circulatory system? ☐ yes ☐ no Why or why not?

  _____

  - Explain why being forced to lie on its back would cause death for a crayfish.

  _____

- Do crayfish have red blood? ☐ yes ☐ no If not, what color is their blood? (You will need to do research to find the answer. Observing a preserved specimen is not sufficient.) _____

The Reproductive Structures

I. Look between the digestive glands (described in the next section) to find the reproductive structures.
- If your crayfish is a male, look for a small pair of white gonads (*testes*) and coiled ducts.
- If your crayfish is a female, look for a large mass of dark-colored *eggs* (inside the ovaries). (Figure 16-5 on p. 373 of your text is an illustration of a female.)

II. Remove these reproductive structures so that you can see the digestive structures.

The Digestive Structures

I. The two light-colored masses extending along each side of the body cavity beyond the cervical groove are the *digestive glands*. What is their function?

_____

II. To expose the *intestine*, insert the point of the scissors underneath the dorsal side of the exoskeleton covering the abdomen. Cut posteriorly to the telson.
- Open the abdominal exoskeleton along the cut. The intestine appears as a tube on the dorsal side of the abdominal muscles.
- Do not confuse the intestine with the dark-colored dorsal blood vessel.

III. Trace the intestine anteriorly to the portion of the cephalothorax where the intestine joins the large, thin-walled *stomach*.

The Viscera

I. Remove most of the internal organs (viscera) of the crayfish by following these instructions.
- Just behind the eyes, cut the bands of muscles leading to the stomach. These muscles hold the stomach in place.
- Pull the stomach posteriorly and cut the short esophagus located just below the stomach.

II. Carefully lift out the organs all in one piece. What is attached to the organs that keeps them all together?

_____

The Excretory Structures

I. Clean out the remaining tissue in the head to expose the *green glands* (kidneys) just posterior to and below the antennules. They are soft, small, and only slightly green.

II. If you are careful, you may also be able to find the small, saclike bladder, which is connected to the green glands.

The Nervous System

I. At the front of the head cavity, between the eyes, note the brain, a tiny mass of white tissue.

II. Trace the nerves that go from the brain to the antennae and the eyes.

III. Trace the *nerve cord* back from the brain to the abdomen by cutting the hard tissue on the floor of the thorax with the scalpel.

- Spread the abdomen apart and pull out the large muscles. (This is the portion of the shrimp, lobster, and fresh crayfish that we eat.)

- The nerve cord should now be exposed on the ventral side of the abdomen.

- The swollen portions of the nerve cord are called the _____.

IV. Why is it an advantage for the crayfish to have its nerve cord on the ventral side rather than on the dorsal side, as it is in humans?

_____

A Drawing of the Dissected Crayfish

I. Do not begin these drawings until after you have completed your dissection.

II. In the crayfish outlines in Area B, draw a dorsal view of the viscera of your specimen. Let different outlines include different body segments so that the organs will not overlap in your drawings (suggested combinations: digestive/excretory, reproductive/circulatory, nervous/respiratory). Label all of the structures that you are able to identify from the dissection instructions.

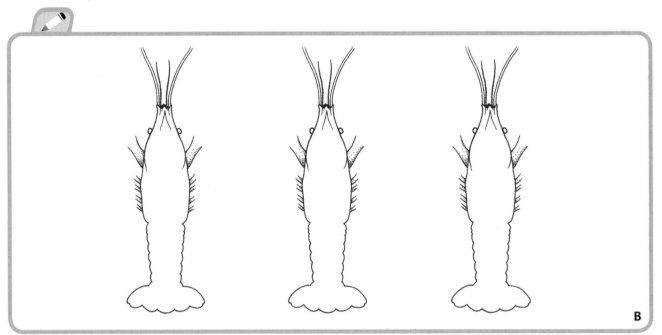

B

Life Processes Chart: Crayfish

I. Fill out a Life Processes Chart for the crayfish.

- Be careful not to repeat material covered in the anatomy sections of this laboratory exercise.

- Include an extensive Other Notes section in your Life Processes Chart.

II. Add to your Life Processes Chart a final section called Other Crustaceans.

- Choose two of the following: *Cyclops*, ostracod (seed shrimp), *Daphnia*, pill bug, barnacle, fiddler crab, brine shrimp (*Artemia*), blue crab, edible shrimp, lobster.

- Do research in another source about the two crustaceans you choose. Then write one or two paragraphs covering their unusual features, their habitats, and their economic and environmental importance.

- If other preserved crustaceans or microscope slides for some of the microcrustaceans are available, observe them and include a description comparing them to the crayfish.

16b   The Grasshopper

name: _____

section: _____ date: _____

Introduction

The order Orthoptera, the straight-winged insects, includes the grass-hopper, cricket, and cockroach. Because of its large size, the lubber grasshopper is often used in the science laboratory. It is native to the states on the Gulf Coast. Its wings are small compared to its body, making the lubber unable to fly.

Goal

✓ Observe the major insect characteristics as seen in the grasshopper

Materials

preserved specimen of lubber grasshopper (*Romalea microptera*)

dissection kit

External Anatomy of the Grasshopper

I. Examine the preserved specimen, taking care not to dissect or damage the specimen in any way. Locate all the following structures. Use a hand lens if necessary.

- Antennae (Note the segments of the antennae and compare the length of the antennae to the grasshopper's body length.)

- Compound eyes

- Simple eyes

  □ The simple eyes are located between the compound eyes.

  □ How many simple eyes are there? (Research may be necessary.) _____

- Thorax

- Head

- Tympanum—What is the purpose of the tympanum? _____

- Jumping legs—Identify these parts of the leg, beginning at the base (the part closest to the body) and progressing toward the tip.

  □ Trochanter

  □ Femur

  □ Tibia

  □ Tarsus (the foot)—Which section of the leg is the largest? _____

- Forelegs—How do the forelegs and the jumping legs differ?

  □ In appearance: _____

  □ In function: _____

- Forewings—The forewings are thick, heavy wings that are not used in flight. What is their purpose?

  _____

- Hind wings—You may need to lift the forewings in order to see these structures. Look for the fine veins in the hind wings.

- Abdomen

- Spiracles—Where are the spiracles located? _____

- Ovipositor—Does your organism have an ovipositor?   ☐ yes   ☐ no

- What does the answer to the previous question indicate? _____

II. On Figure 16b-1, label all the external structures listed above. (NOTE: You will need to draw in details in order to label all the structures.)

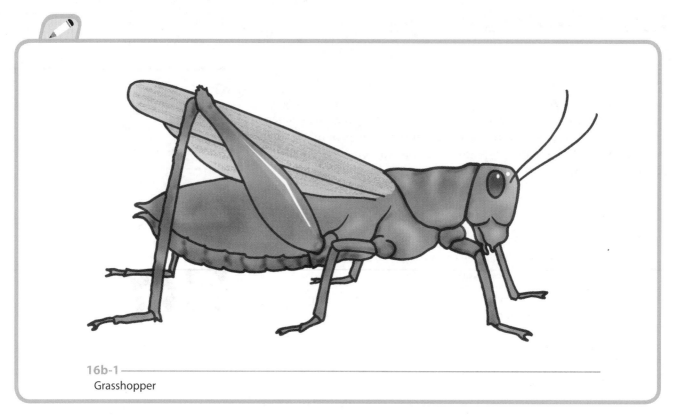

16b-1
Grasshopper

III. On your specimen, locate all the mouthparts listed below.

- Label the mouthparts on Figure 16b-2.

- In the spaces below, tell how many of each mouthpart the grasshopper has.

  □ Labrum: _____

  □ Mandible (jaw): _____

  □ Labium: _____

  □ Labial palp: _____

  □ Maxilla: _____

  □ Maxillary palp: _____

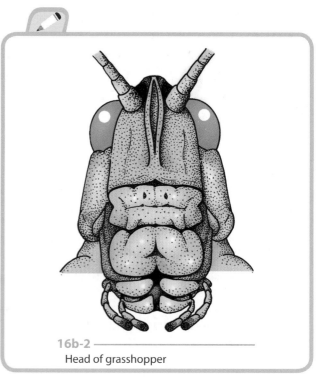

16b-2
Head of grasshopper

Life Processes Chart: Grasshopper

R E O

I. Read Section 16B in your text and take notes on the grasshopper and other members of the order Orthoptera. Do additional research in another text.

II. Fill out a Life Processes Chart and include all the information you learned in this laboratory exercise. Do not copy from the exercise.

16c Insect Orders

Introduction

The majority of organisms in the animal kingdom are insects. In class Insecta, there are over thirty orders, representing hundreds of thousands of different species. The population of each species is thousands to billions. In the first part of this exercise, you will study the major orders of insects (based on number of species) to survey this diverse group.

In many respects, insects compete with man for dominance on the land's surface. In the second part of this exercise, you will observe living insect cultures. Following these observations, you will be given information about the role of insects as pests and how they are controlled. You will then draw some conclusions about controlling insects by reasoning from the information given in this laboratory exercise and from the observations you make of the insect cultures.

Goals

✓ Learn about some of the diversity among insects

✓ Use and enhance research, writing, and oral skills

✓ Learn how insects affect man

✓ Learn about some of the techniques man uses to control insects

✓ Learn about insect metamorphosis

Materials

library or Internet access

visuals of insects

live cultures of fruit flies (*Drosophila melanogaster*) and flour beetles (*Tribolium* sp.)

Reports on Insect Orders

Written Reports on Insect Orders

I. Prepare a written report on any three of the following insect orders.

- Coleoptera
- Lepidoptera
- Hymenoptera
- Diptera
- Orthoptera
- Odonata

II. Follow these guidelines.

- The report for each insect order should be one or two pages in length or the length assigned by your teacher. (One side of a sheet of paper, typed or handwritten, is a page.)

- Much of the information you will need is available from encyclopedias or the Internet.

- Begin your report with a description of the order.
  - □ Indicate the number of wings.
  - □ Indicate the type of mouthparts.
  - □ Indicate the type of metamorphosis.
  - □ Indicate the type of eyes.
  - □ Indicate the special characteristics that set this order apart from the others.
  - □ Do not repeat phylum or class characteristics unless they are greatly modified in the particular order.

- Choose two insects as examples of the order and describe them. You may include a description of the following, if applicable, as you describe each example.
  - □ Habitat
  - □ Life cycle (if interesting or unusual)
  - □ Food
  - □ Economic and personal relationships to man (pet, pest, beneficial, or harmful insect; diseases carried by it; competition with man for food)
  - □ Social instincts

Oral Reports on Insect Orders

The class will be divided into small report groups of two or three students. Each group will be assigned an insect order and will prepare an oral report to present to the class. Your teacher will give you a time limit.

    I.   Follow the guidelines given for the written report, choosing material that will be interesting and valuable to the class.

   II.   Prepare at least one visual aid.

 III.   Choose one or two people to do the speaking.

 IV.   Practice the presentation. Be sure to time the presentation and to adjust it to fit the criteria given by your teacher.

  V.   On the day of your report, give your teacher a list of the contributions of each group member.

Insect Metamorphosis and Control

Flour Beetles

The flour beetle (*Tribolium* sp.) is found in stored grains and sometimes in packaged foods such as cake mixes. Often it becomes a serious pest.

    I.   Observe the living culture of the flour beetle.

- What type of metamorphosis does the flour beetle have?   ☐ complete   ☐ incomplete

- Name and describe the stages of the beetle's life cycle that you were able to find in the culture.

   _____

   _____

   _____

- From your observation, to what insect order do flour beetles belong?

   _____

- In Area A, draw the various stages of the flour beetle's life cycle that you were able to observe. Draw the stages in proportion and label them.

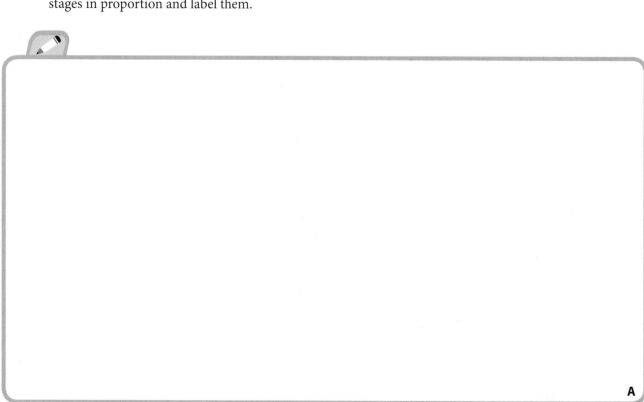

A

II. An infestation of flour beetles in a large grain elevator could cause thousands of dollars' worth of damage. How would you control these pests?

- At what stage(s) in its life cycle would the flour beetle probably be easiest to control?

  ☐ egg ☐ larva ☐ pupa ☐ adult Why?

  _____

- Would it be advisable to put in the flour beetle's medium (grain) a type of chemical insecticide that has to be eaten by the insects to kill them? ☐ yes ☐ no Why or why not?

  _____

  _____

- Some gases (such as carbon dioxide, carbon disulfide, ammonia, and carbon tetrachloride) can be blown through the medium as fumigants to kill flour beetles. Why would fumigants be a more desirable form of control for flour beetles than a liquid spray or dust insecticide? Give at least two reasons.

  _____

  _____

  _____

  _____

- Flour beetles can be killed by keeping them at a temperature of 49 °C (120 °F) for two hours. Which method (fumigation or heat) would be practical for grain storage elevators to use? Which would be practical in the home?

  _____

  _____

  _____

  _____

Fruit Flies and How to Control Them

The fruit fly (*Drosophila* sp.) can be easily seen buzzing around almost any ripe (or more likely, overripe) fruit that is not being refrigerated. These small flies, although more of a nuisance than actual pests, can be a problem for a fruit transporter.

I. Observe the living culture of fruit flies.

- What type of metamorphosis does the fruit fly have? ☐ complete ☐ incomplete
- Name and describe the stages of the fruit fly's life cycle you found in the culture.

  _____

  _____

  _____

  _____

- From your observation, to what insect order do fruit flies belong?

  _____

- In Area B, draw the various stages of the fruit fly's life cycle that you were able to observe. Make sure the stages are drawn in proportion and labeled.

II. Study the control of fruit flies.

- At what stage(s) in its life cycle would the fruit fly probably be easiest to control?

  ☐ egg   ☐ larva   ☐ pupa   ☐ adult   Why?

  _____

- Although fruit flies can be killed with heat, the 49 °C (120 °F) that kills flour beetles only stops the growth of fruit flies; it does not kill them. What drawbacks does control by increased temperature have?

  _____

  _____

- Lowered temperatures are more advisable than raised temperatures for controlling fruit flies. What drawbacks might lowering the temperature have?

  _____

- Would a liquid spray or dust insecticide be advisable? (Recall your observation of the insect's life cycle and how the various stages feed.)   ☐ yes   ☐ no   Why or why not?

  _____

  _____

- To prevent mold and other problems, producers transport softer fruits (which are preferred by fruit flies) in open boxes or boxes with air holes. These boxes allow an infestation of fruit flies in one area to spread quickly to another. In this situation, what drawbacks do fumigants have as a control method?

  _____

  _____

- After seeing the drawbacks of the methods most frequently used to control pests in foods, give another possible method of fruit fly control. Describe its advantages and disadvantages.

  _____

  _____

  _____

17a   Live Bony Fish

Introduction

Class Osteichthyes, the bony fish, is one of the largest vertebrate classes. From your observation of living fish, you will see how a fish uses its specialized structures in its environment.

Although there is great similarity among most fish, there is also some surprising diversity. The members of this class demonstrate delicacy as well as brute strength. Their fins often have unusual and intricate forms, and their body shapes take many different forms.

Studying a Living Fish

Observe the movements of fish swimming in an aquarium. Note the different body movements of various fish. Also note the different body and fin structures in each fish. Base your answers for the questions below on observations of a typical fish (one without major body modifications) found in the aquarium. Remember that you are to observe the natural movements of the fish; do not tap on the glass.

Goals

✓ Observe the motion of fish

✓ Note specialized structures that equip the fish for its environment

✓ Observe the external anatomy of the fish

Materials

living fish

Body Shape

I. Describe the body shape as viewed from the side.

_____

_____

II. Describe the body shape as viewed from the front.

_____

_____

III. In what ways is the fish's body ideally suited for its aquatic environment?

_____

_____

Movements of the Mouth and Opercula

I. Describe the position of the opercula when the mouth is open.

_____

II. Describe the position of the opercula when the mouth is closed.

_____

III. Why are these movements in the fish important?

_____

Eyes and Eyelids

I. Are eyelids present?   ☐ yes   ☐ no

How movable are the eyes in their sockets?

_____

II. The pupils are large. Why is this important to the fish?

_____

Fins

I. Study the fins closely and determine their number, location, and function. Using information from your text and observations of live fish, fill in the Fish Fins chart below.

Fish Fins

Name of Fin	Number	Location	Function
pectoral			
pelvic			
anterior dorsal			
posterior dorsal			
anal			
caudal			

II. When the fish is not moving, which fins move to keep it in position?

_____

_____

_____

_____

III. Observe the fish closely as it rapidly swims forward. What provides the main thrust?

☐ caudal fin ☐ pectoral fins ☐ pelvic fins

Why is this fin or fins more suitable for providing thrust than the other fins?

_____

_____

_____

_____

🏠 Researching the Bony Fish

Unusual Modifications of the Fish's Body and Fin Structure

Read completely the material in your text concerning fish. Do research to find at least two unusual body and fin modifications found in some fish and the purposes they serve. Do not use examples given in the text or in class.

R E O

I. Body modifications

1. Body modification:

_____

Function:

_____

2. Body modification:

_____

Function:

_____

R E O

II. Fin modifications

1. Fin modification:

_____

Function:

_____

2. Fin modification:

_____

Function:

_____

R E O

Life Processes Chart: Yellow Perch

I. Do not repeat the material covered in Studying a Living Fish.

II. Do cover the following materials.

- Scales of the fish
- Muscles of the fish
- Internal structures of the fish (Be sure to describe the structure and function of those items italicized in the dissection section on pp. 163–64 of Lab 17b.)

R E O

Report

I. Choose two other fish that interest you, research them, and write a brief report on each one.

II. These may be saltwater, freshwater, or aquarium fish. Include in each report any adaptation or behavior that makes the fish unusual.

III. Each report must be at least one hundred words but not more than two pages.

17b   Dissection of a Bony Fish

Introduction

Observation of a preserved fish will permit you to see many external structures that are not visible on a live specimen. The internal structures of a fish are typical of vertebrates, and fish dissection can be useful in illustrating and learning these structures.

R E O *External Structures of a Yellow Perch*

Using a preserved specimen of the yellow perch, examine the structures listed below.

I. Mouth

- Describe the teeth.

  _____

  _____

- Tell why the type and placement of the teeth are important to the feeding habits of the yellow perch.

  _____

  _____

  _____

- Examine the tongue. Describe its texture, location, and attachment to the mouth.

  _____

  _____

- Examine the esophageal opening. Insert your probe into it. Explain the need a perch has for a large, elastic esophageal opening.

  _____

II. Nostrils

- Where are the nostrils located?

  _____

- Describe the structure of the nostrils.

  _____

III. Fins

- Raise the dorsal fins by pulling them forward. The dorsal fins of a yellow perch consist of a spiny and a soft portion.

  ▫ To determine whether a structure in a fin is a ray or a spine, put your finger on the very tip of the structure and then push on it. A spine will not bend; a ray bends.

  ▫ How many spines are there on your specimen's dorsal anterior fin? _____

  ▫ Compare the number you counted with the number of spines on other specimens. Is the number the same?   ☐ yes   ☐ no

  If the answer is no, how wide is the variation? _____

> **Goal**
> ✓ Observe the external and internal anatomy of the fish

> **Materials**
> preserved fish (yellow perch)
> culture dish
> hand lens or stereomicroscope
> dissection pan
> dissection kit
> plastic bag
>

- Tell whether the other fins on the yellow perch are supported by rays or spines or both.

  Pectoral: ☐ rays ☐ spines ☐ both

  Pelvic: ☐ rays ☐ spines ☐ both

  Anal: ☐ rays ☐ spines ☐ both

  Caudal: ☐ rays ☐ spines ☐ both

  Anterior Dorsal: ☐ rays ☐ spines ☐ both

  Posterior Dorsal: ☐ rays ☐ spines ☐ both

IV. Body covering

- Locate the lateral line. What function does it serve?

  _____

- Carefully examine a scale from the yellow perch with a stereomicroscope or with a hand lens. What structures are you able to observe?

  _____

V. Opercula and gills

- Raise the right operculum, and with a probe carefully separate the layers of gills to examine them. How many layers of gills are there? _____ Is this true of both sides? ☐ yes ☐ no

- Insert your probe through the gills and into the mouth cavity. Note where it enters the mouth. Why is the mouth–gill chamber opening necessary?

  _____

  _____

- With scissors, cut the left operculum away and remove one set of gills by cutting the upper and lower attachments of the *gill arch*.

- Rinse the gills and place them in a culture dish filled with water; examine them closely. Examine the feathery *filaments* and the comblike *rakers*.

- Examine the upper and lower ends of the arch and try to find the blood vessels that enter and leave the gill. Why should the gill be so richly supplied with blood?

  _____

- Draw a gill in Area A. Label all the parts italicized above.

Figure 17b-1 is an outline of a yellow perch. Draw in the external structures not shown and label as many of the external parts as you can.

A

17b-1 ―――――――――――――――――――――――――

External structures of the yellow perch

name: _____

Internal Structures of a Yellow Perch

Read the entire section on dissecting the perch before you begin to cut. Note carefully the diagrams you are to draw. You should include all the following italicized terms in your Life Processes Chart of the yellow perch (Lab 17a). Do the remainder of this lab in sequence.

I. Open the body cavity.

- Hold your fish with ventral side up, head pointing away from you. Insert your scissors through the body wall in front of (anterior to) the anus; then cut along the midline of the body to the area between the gill covers on the lower side of the head.

- Lay your fish on its right side (with the head toward your left). Continue the incision from the point between the gills, around the front of the operculum, to the top of the body cavity. (A good portion of the dorsal side of the fish is a muscle layer. You need to cut only to the top of the swim bladder.)

- Make another incision close to the anus and cut dorsally to the top of the body cavity.

- With your scalpel, make the remaining incision across the body cavity (just dorsal to the swim bladder).

- Remove the side wall of the body. The removal of the wall will reveal the body cavity with the organs in their normal positions.

II. Locate the internal organs.

- The digestive system

  □ Locate the beige *liver*. It is in the anterior end of the body cavity. Gently raise the lobes of the liver and find the *gallbladder* (which looks like a very tiny, flattened balloon) attached to the lower surface of the liver. Cut the liver free and remove it in one piece, if possible.

  □ Locate the short *esophagus* and *stomach*.

  □ Locate the *intestine* and follow its loops to the *anus*.

  □ Cut the esophagus where it enters the mouth and cut the intestine near the anus.

  □ Remove the digestive system without disturbing the other organs and place it beside the fish in the dissection pan.

  □ Draw in Area B the digestive system as it lies outside the body cavity. Label all the organs italicized above as well as the *pyloric ceca*.

  □ Cut open the stomach. Can you recognize any specific food?   ☐ yes ☐ no
    If yes, what? _____

- The urogenital system

  □ With the alimentary canal removed, you should see the *gonads* and perhaps the *urinary bladder*.

    ♦ The female perch may have a large, yellow orange *ovary* (called a *roe*) containing many eggs. (If your fish was about to lay eggs, you may have already removed this structure in order to see the other organs.) The ovary could also be a small, beige, drumstick-shaped structure if the fish was not ready to lay eggs.

B

- ♦ The male perch will have small, cream-colored *testes*.
    - ▫ Trace the white threadlike ducts coming from the gonads and the small tube from the urinary bladder to the *urogenital opening*.
    - ▫ Find the *kidneys*, which usually are dark red strands along the spine.
- • The swim bladder and the circulatory system
    - ▫ Locate the *swim bladder* along the top of the body cavity. It may have broken when you removed the body wall.
    - ▫ On the ventral side of the body cavity, near the opercula, locate the *pericardial cavity*, which contains the *heart*.
        - ♦ The soft upper chamber of the heart is the *atrium*.
        - ♦ Below and anterior to the atrium is the *ventricle*.
        - ♦ A purplish, muscular bulb, the *bulbus arteriosus*, gives rise to the *ventral aorta*, which branches to the gills.
    - ▫ Remove the heart and draw it in Area C. Label as many structures as you can.
- • The nervous system
    - ▫ Expose the brain of the fish.
        - ♦ Hold the fish with its dorsal side up and position its head so that it points away from you. Using your scalpel and scissors, cut away the skin from the skull.
        - ♦ Scrape the skull with your scissors to wear away the bone.
        - ♦ When the bone becomes thin, pick away the bone with the forceps to expose the brain.
    - ▫ Locate the *olfactory lobes* in front, the larger lobes of the *cerebrum* behind these, and the very large *optic lobes* posterior to the cerebrum. The *cerebellum* is posterior to the optic lobes, and the *medulla oblongata*, an enlargement of the spinal cord, is posterior to the cerebellum and slightly underneath it.
        - ♦ Considering the size and function of each brain part, in what function should the fish be most adept? _____
        Is the fish most adept at this function? ☐ yes ☐ no
        Explain. _____
        - ♦ When you consider the size and function of each brain part, in what function should it be least adept? _____
        Is the fish least adept at this function? ☐ yes ☐ no
        Explain. _____
    - ▫ Draw the nervous system in Area D and label the brain regions and the spinal cord as you found them.

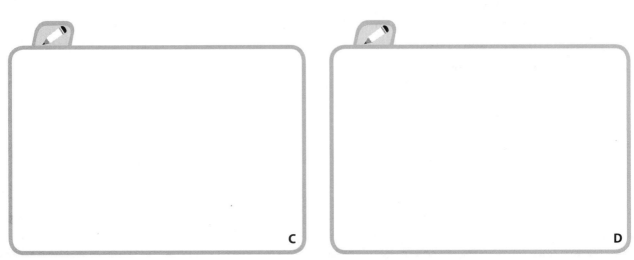

C

D

18a Birds

Introduction

The class Aves contains warm-blooded vertebrates that hatch from eggs—the birds. They are the only animals with feathers. After observing these remarkably strong yet lightweight structures, you will study a chicken egg, which will reveal the major components of bird eggs. Then you will be asked to learn about the birds found in your area.

Goals

✓ Examine the body coverings of birds

✓ Learn about the physical characteristics that enable birds to fly

✓ Observe parts of a typical egg

✓ Learn about local birds

Observing Bird Feathers

R E O

I. Obtain a down feather and contour feathers (include a flight feather and a body feather).

- Examine the feather structures described on page 429 of the text.

- What observations can you make regarding the differences between a body feather and a flight feather?

  _____

  _____

- Holding a flight feather at the base, use the thumb and forefinger of your other hand to pinch the vane near the top and then slide your fingers down, separating the vane. Next, use the same fingers to smooth the feather back into correct position by rubbing the other direction.

  What parts of the feather allow it to be repaired?

  _____

  What term is used to describe a bird's repairing its feathers using only its beak?

  _____

R E O

II. Examine a preserved slide of down and contour feathers under a microscope.

- Can you see barbs, barbules, and hooks on the contour feathers?
  ☐ yes   ☐ no

- Can you see all of these structures on the down feathers?
  ☐ yes   ☐ no

  Explain why all of these structures are or are not necessary on a down feather.

  _____

  _____

R E O

III. In Area A, draw and label a section of a bird feather as seen through the microscope. Draw a section large enough to show the shaft, barbs, and barbules.

Materials

microscope

feathers (contour, including body and flight; down)

preserved slides of feathers (contour and down)

raw chicken egg

dissection pan

dissection kit

hand lens

A

Dissecting a Bird Egg

I. Place a raw chicken egg in a dish or dissection pan.

II. Using a probe, carefully break into the larger, more rounded end. Using tweezers, chip away the hard shell to expose the air space.

What separates this air space from the liquid contents of the egg? _____

III. Using tweezers, begin to chip away the hard outer shell, starting at the air space and continuing along one side.

IV. When you have exposed most of one side—still enclosed by a membrane—use your scissors to cut into the membrane to reveal the contents.

What is the large yellow mass called? _____

What is the purpose for this material? _____

Can you see an embryo growing here? ☐ yes ☐ no

Why or why not?

_____

What is the clear material in the egg called? _____

In addition to water, what is a primary component of this clear material? _____

V. See if you can identify the thickened, whitish bands connecting the yolk to each end of the egg.

What are these bands called? _____

What is their function?

_____

What might happen to the developing chick if these bands do not form or function properly?

_____

_____

_____

VI. Examine part of the eggshell with a magnifying glass. You should be able to see tiny pores. Why would these pores be present?

_____

Studying Local Birds

I. Prepare a list of three birds native to your area.

II. Write a description of each bird.

- Each description should be about one page long.
- Include in each description the following details.
    □ Size of bird; coloration; type of beak, wings, legs, and feet
    □ Food, feeding time, seasonal changes in diet
    □ Preferred nesting sites, description of nest and eggs, number of young, incubation period, time of year the young hatch, amount of parental care, whether young are altricial or precocial
    □ Migration—if, where, and when it goes; if nonmigratory, how it survives the winter
    □ Population status and protection level if endangered or threatened
    □ Ecological significance—whether the bird helps or harms human interests
- Obtain illustrations of each bird if possible and include them with your reports.

18b   Mammals

Introduction

Like birds, mammals are endothermic, but they are characterized by fur rather than feathers. They are the animals that have body characteristics and intelligence most like man's and make a fascinating study. In this lab you will examine different kinds of mammal fur and compare it to your own hair. You will also examine an unidentified mammal skull to learn what its form indicates about its function. Finally, you will do some research to learn about some mammals from your area.

> **Goals**
> ✓ Examine mammal fur and compare it to human hair
> ✓ Observe parts of a mammal skull
> ✓ Learn about local mammals

> **Materials**
> hand lens or stereomicroscope
> microscope
> mirror
> slide
> cover slip
> mammal fur
> unidentified mammal skull
> ruler
>
>

Observing Fur

I. Use a hand lens or stereomicroscope to examine guard hair and underhair.

II. Compare fur and hair.

- Prepare a wet mount of a guard hair, an underhair, and a hair from your head.

- What differences do you notice between guard hair, underhair, and human scalp hair?

_____

_____

_____

Examining a Skull

I. Select a skull from those that are available. The letter identifying my skull is _____.

With a ruler, measure the skull's length and width (at its widest point) to the nearest millimeter and record your findings: _____ mm in length and _____ mm in width

II. Locate the opening where the spinal cord enters the brain cavity at the back of the skull. Measure the diameter of this opening: _____ mm

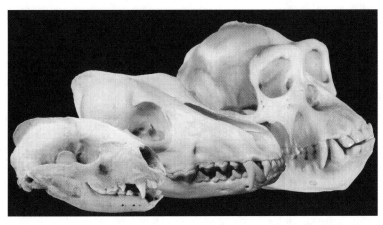

18b-1
The skulls of a badger, a coyote, and a chimpanzee demonstrate the variety among mammals.

III. Examine the skull to find where the ear canals and nostrils enter the skull. Considering the placement and size of these spaces, answer the following questions.

How important might hearing be to this mammal?

_____

How important might smelling be to this mammal?

_____

IV. Find the eye sockets (orbits).

- Identify the largest opening at the back of each socket. What might be the function of this opening?

_____

- Predators usually have eyes that are directed more toward the front, while prey species often have their eyes oriented toward the sides. Why might God have made them this way?

_____

_____

_____

- Which of these categories would your mammal belong to?   ☐ predator   ☐ prey

- Nocturnal species often have eyes that are proportionally larger than diurnal species to allow for better nighttime vision. Do you think your mammal is a nocturnal species?   ☐ yes ☐ no

V. Examine the teeth of your mammal skull and record the number of teeth that would fit into each of these three general categories (if some teeth are missing and you see only sockets, try to determine their type based on the teeth that remain).

_____ incisors   _____ canines   _____ molars

- Based on the number, size, and arrangement of the teeth on the skull, would you say this mammal is an herbivore, carnivore, or omnivore? _____

- After washing your hands, count the teeth in your own mouth and record the numbers here. Use a mirror if necessary.

_____ incisors   _____ canines   _____ molars

🏠 Studying Local Mammals

I. Prepare a list of three mammals native to your area.

- Be specific. (The term *mouse* is not specific enough. *Field mouse* and *deer mouse* are specific enough for this exercise.)
- Try to list mammals from three different orders.

II. Write a brief description of each mammal.

- Each description should be about one page long.
- Include in each description the following details.
  - ☐ Type of teeth, food, feeding time, seasonal changes in diet
  - ☐ Preferred home sites, type of home built, number of young, time of year young are born, time it takes young to mature
  - ☐ What the animal does during the various seasons
  - ☐ Ecological significance—whether the mammal helps or harms human interests
- Obtain illustrations of each mammal if possible and include them with your reports.

19 Succession and Pollution

Introduction

Succession is the predictable change of a biotic community over a period of time. Succession progresses through a series of stages to the climax stage for that particular area. In this exercise you will set up an ecosystem in a container. A small artificial environment is sometimes called a microcosm. A microcosm will progress through various stages and, if permitted to continue long enough, will conclude in a climax. Unless the microcosm is managed by human intervention in the later stages of succession, the artificiality will result in the death (one form of climax) of all the organisms. Lack of space and lack of a wide enough variety of populations in the microcosm prevent the complete cycling of the various substances that exist in natural ecosystems.

Natural succession of an area can, however, be altered by intervention. In the second part of this laboratory exercise, several microcosms will be set up, different factors introduced, and the successions taking place in the microcosms compared.

Setting Up an Aquatic Microcosm

- Clean a one-gallon aquarium or a jar with a lid. Use salt as a cleansing agent to make sure there is no soap film.
- Fill the container half-full of sterile (boiled) pond or spring water.
- Place a handful of dried grass, leaves, or other plant material obtained from the edge of a pond into the water.
- Cover the container (a piece of glass placed over the opening is good) and set it in a well-lighted area (not in direct sunlight).

Goals

✓ Observe succession in a microcosm
✓ Observe the effects of various pollutants upon succession

Materials

sterile (boiled) pond or spring water
dried plant material from a pond
small aquariums or large (quart) jars with lids
microscope
pipets
slides
cover slips
fertilizer
algal cultures
protozoan cultures
baking soda
vinegar
powdered lime
universal pH test papers (for range 1–14)
hydrochloric acid

Observing Succession in an Aquatic Microcosm

I. After the aquatic microcosm has been set up for two or three days, make the following observations and record the data you obtain on a classroom chart like the one illustrated on page 171.

- Record statistics about the microcosm.
  - ▫ Do not disturb the microcosm as you make these observations.
  - ▫ Record the temperature (without stirring the microcosm).
  - ▫ Place a drop of the microcosm on a universal pH test paper. Record the pH.
  - ▫ Turbidity is the cloudiness of the water. Indicate not only how cloudy the water is but also what color it is.
- Record statistics about the organisms in the microcosm.
  - ▫ Groups of students will be assigned to make and observe wet mounts from different areas of the microcosm.
    - ♦ One group will obtain the material for its wet mount from the surface of the microcosm, another group from the middle, and another from the bottom. Disturb the microcosm as little as possible.

♦ Although each group may make and observe several slides, only one entry for each microcosmic area should be made on the chart.

▫ Identify as many of the organisms as you can.

♦ Use a pictorial key to identify pond organisms or protozoans, if necessary.

♦ If you cannot locate the name of an organism you have found, make a reference sketch of it and assign it a number.

♦ Record the name or number of the organism on the chart and indicate whether the organism was very abundant, abundant, rare, or very rare in the material on your slide.

▫ Do a specimen count.

♦ With a microscope focused on the populated area of your slide, count for fifteen seconds the organisms you see in your microscope field. Include any that move into the field while you are counting as well as those that were there when you started.

♦ Moving the slide slightly each time to a new field of view, repeat the procedure three more times.

♦ Average your results and record your fifteen-second specimen count on the classroom chart.

II. Every other day for two or three weeks, repeat the observations and record your results on the chart. You should be able to complete this during the first few minutes of class.

III. Answer the following questions concerning your class's observations.

- Number of organisms

  ▫ As the microcosm progresses toward its climax stage, how does its population change?

  ☐ increases   ☐ decreases

  ▫ As the microcosm progresses toward its climax, are there more or fewer types of organisms?

  ☐ more   ☐ fewer

  ▫ What progression of the number and type of organisms would you expect in an ecosystem passing through succession?

  _____

  _____

  Did your microcosm follow this progression?   ☐ yes   ☐ no

- Types of organisms

  ▫ What types of organisms are most abundant in the pioneer stages?

  _____

  ▫ What types of organisms are most abundant as the microcosm approaches climax?

  _____

  ▫ Is this progression of organism types what you would expect in an ecosystem passing through succession?   ☐ yes   ☐ no

  Why or why not?

  _____

  _____

  _____

  _____

- Conclusions
  - ☐ What can you conclude about the progression of the relative sizes of the individual organisms during succession?

    _____

    _____

  - ☐ What is the effect of the turbidity and pH of the microcosm on its number of organisms and its succession?

    _____

    _____

    _____

Microcosm Observations

Date	Temperature	pH	Turbidity	Organisms	Specimen Count
2/14 Day 3	32°C	8	Little turbidity, white material in water.	Top: 1. (small circular algae)—abundant 2. Paramecium—rare 3. Small flagellate—abundant Middle: 4. Paramecium—rare Bottom: 5. Amoeba—rare 6. Small flagellate—abundant	Top 5 Middle 2 Bottom 8
2/16 Day 5	33°C	8.3	Little turbidity	Top: 1. (small circular algae)—abundant	Top 8

Observing Pollution and Succession

R E O

In an ecosystem passing through succession, a pollutant may be defined as any substance or factor that alters normal succession. In the following exercise you will be asked to add a single pollutant to various microcosms and note how it affects the succession of each microcosm.

I. Prepare an aquatic microcosm as described in the box on page 169.

II. When the microcosm is two or three days old, divide it.

- Thoroughly mix the microcosm to distribute the organisms equally.
- While the culture is mixed, divide it into four or five equal portions. Each portion will make up one small microcosm.
- Place each portion in a jar large enough to be only half filled.

III. Select and introduce pollutants.

- Organisms are a form of pollutant. Introduce to one of the microcosms a few of one type of organism from an individual laboratory culture of algae, protozoans, or small aquatic organisms (*Daphnia*, for example).

- Another way to pollute the microcosms is to introduce a factor that will alter the physical environment. Consider adding a small quantity of one of these: vinegar (an acid), soluble plant food (nutrients), baking soda (a base), powdered lime, or hydrochloric acid. (You may need to add a little more of each substance every few days.)

- Another pollutant is the abundance of a physical environmental factor. Consider placing one of the microcosms in direct sunlight, another in a dark cabinet, and one near a heater or in a cold closet. Also consider adding water to dilute the microcosm by doubling its volume.

- Be sure to keep at least one of the small microcosms as a control and treat it the same way you treated the large microcosm in the previous experiment.

IV. Observe and keep records for each of the small microcosms.

V. Write a summary of the results.

- Write a summary for each microcosm, including its contents and progression.

- Compare the microcosms, pointing out their differences.

- Offer probable explanations for the differences observed in the various microcosms.

_____

_____

_____

_____

_____

_____

_____

_____

_____

_____

_____

_____

_____

_____

_____

_____

_____

_____

_____

_____

_____

_____

_____

_____

20a Readings on the Human Body Systems

Introduction

For this exercise you will read magazine articles on many aspects of each of the human systems. You will then write a brief report on each of these articles. This activity will help you learn more about the human body systems that interest you most.

Assignment

I. Read magazine articles about the human body systems (or parts of the systems).

- Find articles in magazines and on the Internet.

    □ Look in the *Reader's Guide to Periodical Literature*, available in most libraries. Look under such topics as human anatomy or under a particular disease, such as bone cancer or arthritis. (Topics such as skeleton or skeletal system are general, and you may not find articles listed under them.)

    □ Do not report on encyclopedia articles.

    □ Do not read Internet articles that are on nonacademic sites. (If you are not sure about the site, ask your teacher for help.)

    □ Choose an article of three or four pages (not including pictures). If an article is more than eight pages, it can count as two articles.

    □ Recommend good articles to other students. (They must read the article for themselves, of course.)

    □ Stop reading an article that is too simple or too difficult and find another.

- Read one article for each of the eleven human body systems.

- Read extra articles if you wish. Your teacher will inform you of how much the entire assignment is worth and how many points each article is worth.

- Read no more than five articles on any one body system.

II. Write a review of each article.

- Use a separate 3 × 5 card for each article.

- Use only one card for each report. Do not use extra cards to make long reports.

- Follow the format illustrated in Figure 20a-1.

- Provide the following information in this order:

    1. *Title of article* (top line, left side). Indent on the second line if the title is long.

    2. *Human system* (top line, right side). Underline it and then write your name underneath the line.

    3. *Name of author(s)* (second line, left side).

    4. *Name of magazine or website* (third line, left side).

    5. *Date of article's publication*, not the date you read it (third line, right side).

    6. *Page numbers* of article (fourth line, left side). List the page numbers, not how many pages there were.

    7. *Illustrations* (fourth line, right side). List the number and types.

    8. *Material discussed* in the article. Use the remainder of the front side with the first line indented. The back of the card can be used if necessary.

    9. *Evaluation* of the article using the following scale: 1–2 very poor (you learned very little from the article); 3–4 good; 5 excellent. Write your evaluation in the lower right-hand corner and circle it. On the back of the card, write 2–3 sentences explaining why you gave the article that evaluation.

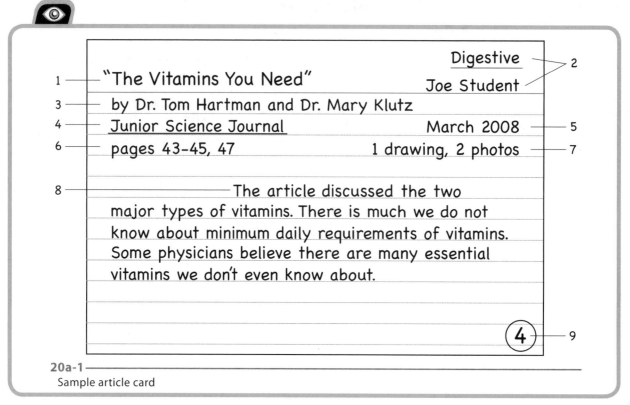

1 — "The Vitamins You Need"

Digestive — 2

Joe Student

3 — by Dr. Tom Hartman and Dr. Mary Klutz

4 — Junior Science Journal   March 2008 — 5

6 — pages 43–45, 47   1 drawing, 2 photos — 7

8 — The article discussed the two major types of vitamins. There is much we do not know about minimum daily requirements of vitamins. Some physicians believe there are many essential vitamins we don't even know about.

④ — 9

20a-1

Sample article card

III. Turn in your reviews.

- Bring the card(s) for each system on the test date for that system. The article is required reading for that test. The card(s) will be checked and returned.

- Turn in the entire collection of article cards when you turn in your laboratory notebook.

It is recommended that a record of the articles you read be kept so that you will know at a glance which ones are yet to be completed. The following table can be used.

System	Required	Extra			
Integumentary	☐	☐	☐	☐	☐
Skeletal	☐	☐	☐	☐	☐
Muscular	☐	☐	☐	☐	☐
Respiratory	☐	☐	☐	☐	☐
Digestive	☐	☐	☐	☐	☐
Circulatory	☐	☐	☐	☐	☐
Lymphatic	☐	☐	☐	☐	☐
Excretory	☐	☐	☐	☐	☐
Nervous	☐	☐	☐	☐	☐
Endocrine	☐	☐	☐	☐	☐
Reproductive	☐	☐	☐	☐	☐

20b The Human Body and the Skeletal System

Introduction

The human body is an outstanding example of God's intricate design in creation. The more we study it, the more we understand that each minute detail has significance. In this laboratory exercise you will learn the names of some of the obvious parts of the body and look at some details regarding the skeletal system.

Terms of Human Anatomy

Label all of the following terms on one (or both) of the diagrams in Figure 20b-1.

I. Direction (indicate by drawing arrows on the diagrams): anterior, posterior, superior, inferior, medial, lateral, transverse, sagittal, deep, superficial, proximal, and distal

II. Cavities: cranial, buccal, nasal, thoracic, abdominal, and pelvic

III. Areas: pectoral, cervical, brachial, lumbar, trunk, thigh, calf, upper extremity, lower extremity, pelvis, and buttocks

Goals

✓ Learn the basic terms associated with anatomy

✓ Observe the typical microstructures and macrostructures of the skeletal system

✓ Learn the names of various bones and joints of the human body

Materials

colored pencils

microscope

preserved slides of dry ground bone, c.s.

model of a human skeleton

skeleton diagrams

library

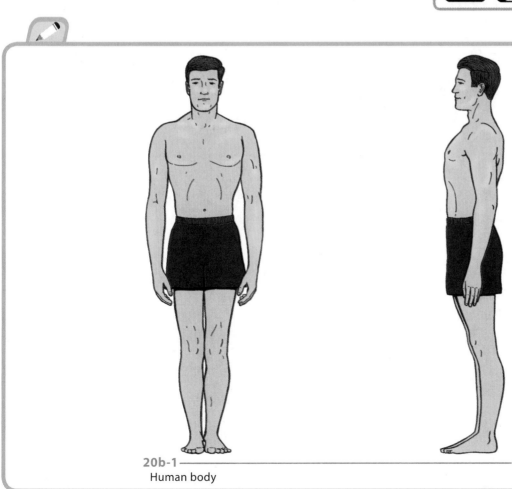

20b-1
Human body

The Skeletal System

The primary system of support is the skeleton. The skeleton includes the bones, ligaments, joints, and cartilage of the body. We will begin with a microscopic study of bone and then proceed to a study of the major structures of the skeleton.

Microstructures

I. Observe the preserved slide of dry ground bone, c.s., and draw a diagram in Area A.

II. Label a complete Haversian system. Include the Haversian canal, lamellae, lacunae, canals, and any other structures observed in the preserved specimen.

Macrostructures

I. Learn the bone names and markings indicated on page 501 of the text. (Omit those indicated by the instructor.)

- Locate these bones on the skeleton in the laboratory.

- Label them if they are shown on Figure 20b-2. Below the diagrams, list the bones not shown.

II. Learn the types of joints. Fill in the missing information on the Joints of the Human Body chart.

A

Joints of the Human Body			
Kind	**Type**	**Movement**	**Examples**
movable	ball-and-socket	free movement inside a cone (circumduction)	1. 2.
		flexion and extension on one plane	1. elbow (humerus, ulna) 2.
	pivot	rotation	1. radius and ulna 2.
movable	gliding		1. thumb 2.
slightly movable	cartilaginous	bending, twisting, and slight compression	1. between vertebrae 2.
immovable	suture or fibrous		1. 2.

name: _____

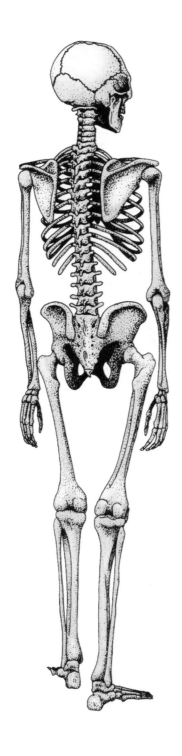

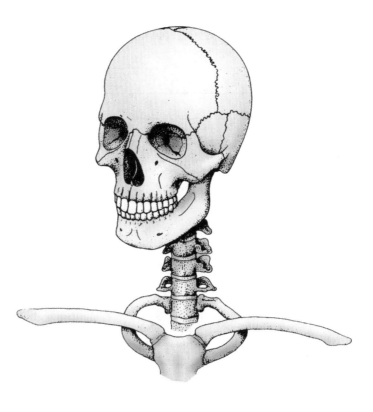

20b-2
Human skeleton

III. Do additional research on sesamoid bones. (NOTE: Although they are not always the same thing, sesamoid bones are sometimes called supernumerary bones.)

- What are sesamoid bones?

  _____

  _____

  _____

- How do they develop?

  _____

  _____

  _____

- List some examples of sesamoid bones.

  _____

  _____

  _____

20c The Human Muscular and Integumentary Systems

Introduction

The human muscular system is a marvel of design. It permits not only movement but also various degrees of strength and extensive flexibility. Human skin is equally marvelous. It is tough enough to block out most substances that would invade our bodies, yet soft enough to permit sensation of minute changes in temperature, touch, and pressure—all this while remaining supple enough to bend almost constantly without breaking. We are truly "wonderfully made" (Ps. 139:14).

Goals

✓ Observe the typical microstructures of the muscular and integumentary systems

✓ Learn the names, origins, insertions, and actions of some of the major human muscles

The Muscular System

The primary system of movement is the muscular system. We will begin by studying the structures of muscular tissue and then study some of the major muscles of the human body.

Microstructures

I. Observe a preserved slide of a section of skeletal muscle. In Area A draw a diagram of what you see. Label all the structures you observe.

II. Observe a preserved slide of a section of visceral muscle. In Area B draw a diagram of what you see. Label all the structures you observe.

Materials

microscope

preserved slides of skeletal (striated) muscle, cardiac muscle, visceral (smooth) muscle, and human skin, c.s.

human muscle diagrams

colored pencils

library

A

B

C

III. Observe a preserved slide of a section of cardiac muscle. In Area C draw a diagram of what you see. Label all the structures you observe.

IV. Fill in the missing spaces in The Three Types of Muscles chart.

The Three Types of Muscles

Type	Other names	Control	Location (L.) and function (F.)
skeletal	1. striated 2. voluntary	☐ conscious ☐ unconscious	L. F.
	1. 2. involuntary	☐ conscious ☐ unconscious	L. F.
	heart	☐ conscious ☐ unconscious	L. F.

Macrostructures

I. Study carefully the information on pages 511–14 of the text regarding the attachments and naming of muscles.

II. Answer the following questions:

- What is the linea alba?

  _____

- Where is it located?

  _____

- Where is the Achilles tendon?

  _____

III. Learn the name, origin, insertion, and action of each of the human muscles listed on page 512 of the text. Include the diaphragm, which is discussed on pages 441 and 520 of the text. Omit those muscles indicated by the instructor.

- The following suggestions are helpful when learning the required muscles:
    □ Locate each of the muscles on your body by putting your hand over it and then performing its action. You should be able to feel the muscle working.
    □ Locate the origin and insertion while you perform the muscle's action. The action should seem logical when you know the origin and insertion.
    □ Consult a human muscle chart to make sure you have located the origin and insertion correctly. Note carefully the location of the muscle.
- On the human body outlines (Figure 20c-1), use colored pencils to sketch and label each of the muscles you are assigned to know. (NOTE: One diagram is a dorsal view, and the other is ventral, but both are in anatomical position.)

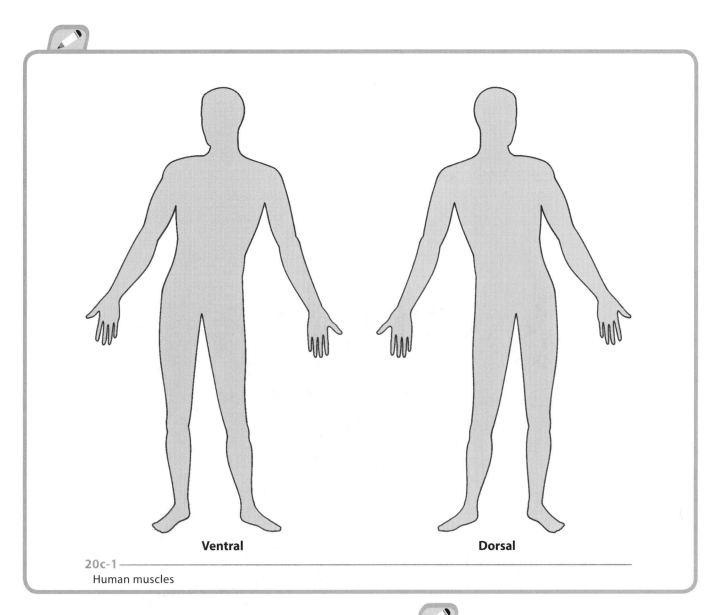

Ventral

Dorsal

20c-1 _____

Human muscles

The Integumentary System

The primary function of the integumentary system is protection. Several types of skin are found on the body. The thick, tough skin of the palms of the hands and the soles of the feet is considerably different from the thin skin of the face, the arms, and the abdomen.

Observe Human Skin

Observe a preserved slide of human skin. In Area D draw and label the structures you are able to identify.

D

Label Structures of Human Skin

Identify and label as many structures as possible in Figure 20c-2.

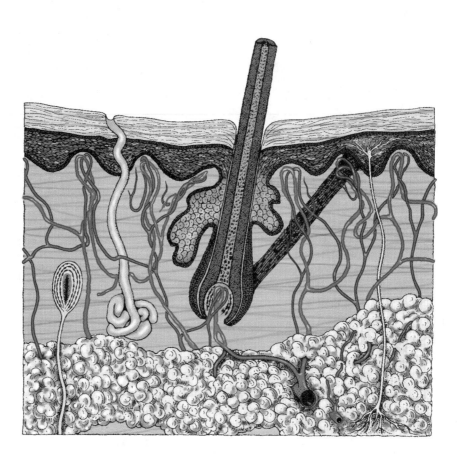

20c-2 —————————————————
A section of typical human skin

Prepare a Report About Human Skin

  I. Read about some skin-related topic or problem.

  • Burns, tans, skin cancer, baldness, warts, moles, birthmarks, oily skin, dry skin, skin transplants, skin wrinkles, aging of the skin, and face-lifts are possible topics.

  • Consult at least three sources and read at least five pages regarding your topic.

 II. Prepare a brief report based on your research.

  • Written reports must be at least one hundred words long and should be submitted with this lab.

  • Oral reports should be from three to five minutes long and will be assigned in place of written reports for some students.

21a The Human Respiratory System

name: _____

section: _____ date: _____

Introduction

The first section of this laboratory exercise will be done as a class demonstration. Various lung volume tests will supply the data to use in answering the questions. Following the lung volume demonstration, there are several exercises that deal with the structures of the respiratory system.

Goals

✓ Measure average lung capacity
✓ Learn structures of the respiratory system

Air Volume Measurement

R E O

A spirometer is a device used to measure the volume of air a person exhales. A long plastic bag calibrated in liters may be used instead of the relatively expensive spirometer. The lung volume bag is not as accurate, but for the purposes of this exercise it will serve well.

Materials

lung volume bag
rubber band
mouthpiece
paper towels
tissues
stethoscope
isopropyl (rubbing) alcohol

Preparing a Lung Volume Bag

I.   Select three students of average size and select an assistant for each.

II. Prepare the lung volume bags.

   • Insert the mouthpiece partway into the open end of the lung volume bag and secure it with a rubber band. (See Figure 21a-1.)

   • Have the assistant sit down.

   • Slide the bag slowly across the assistant's knee while he presses the bag with a paper towel. This will remove all air from the lung volume bag. (See Figure 21a-1.)

Measuring Lung Volume

I.   Measure tidal volume.

   • Instruct the person being tested to breathe in a normal breath, pinch his nose, put the lung volume bag mouthpiece in his mouth, and breathe out a normal breath.

   • Ask the assistant to take the bag and hold it closed while sliding it across his knee and pressing it with a paper towel in order to force all the air to the closed end. Note how many liters of air are in the bag.

   • Record the data on the board. Students should fill in their Lung Volume charts (on the next page) from the data on the board.

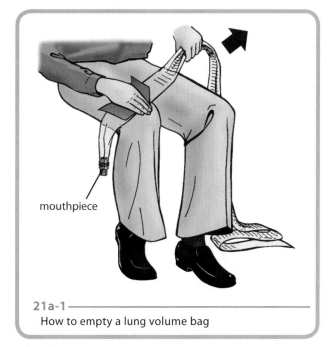

mouthpiece

21a-1
How to empty a lung volume bag

   • Empty the lung volume bag, using the procedure described earlier.

   • Have each person tested perform this experiment two more times. Record each volume in the proper space of the Lung Volume chart.

II. Measure expiratory reserve volume.

   • Have the person being tested breathe in a normal breath, breathe out a normal breath, pinch his nose, put the lung volume bag mouthpiece in his mouth, and breathe out as much as possible.

   • Using the procedure described in the instructions for measuring tidal volume, measure the air and record the reading for each person.

Lung Volume

Tidal volume

Person A	Person B	Person C	Average
1. _____	1. _____	1. _____	_____ mL
2. _____	2. _____	2. _____	or
3. _____	3. _____	3. _____	_____ L

Expiratory reserve volume

Person A	Person B	Person C	Average
1. _____	1. _____	1. _____	_____ mL
2. _____	2. _____	2. _____	or
3. _____	3. _____	3. _____	_____ L

Vital capacity

Person A	Person B	Person C	Average
1. _____	1. _____	1. _____	_____ mL
2. _____	2. _____	2. _____	or
3. _____	3. _____	3. _____	_____ L

- Have each person tested perform this experiment two more times. Record each volume in the proper space of the Lung Volume chart.

III. Measure vital capacity.

- Have the person being tested breathe in as much as he possibly can, pinch his nose, put the lung volume bag mouthpiece in his mouth, and breathe out as much as possible.

- Using the procedure described in the instructions for measuring tidal volume, force the air to the bottom of the bag and record the reading for each person.

- Have each person tested repeat this experiment two more times. Record each volume in the proper space of the Lung Volume chart.

Computing Average Lung Capacities

I. Take all your data and determine averages for the following volumes. (Be careful to use the correct units.)

- Tidal volume: _____ mL

- Expiratory reserve volume: _____ mL

- Vital capacity: _____ mL

II. Using these averages, compute the inspiratory reserve volume: _____ mL

III. Assuming a residual volume of 1000 mL, what would be the average total lung capacity of the people tested? _____ mL

IV. According to the information on page 521 of the text, are these lung volume results considered average? ☐ yes ☐ no   If not, what factors might account for the difference?

_____

_____

_____

name: _____

Structures of the Respiratory System

I. Label Figure 21a-2 as completely as possible.

II. Under each label, indicate what happens to air in that structure. Enclose this information in parentheses.

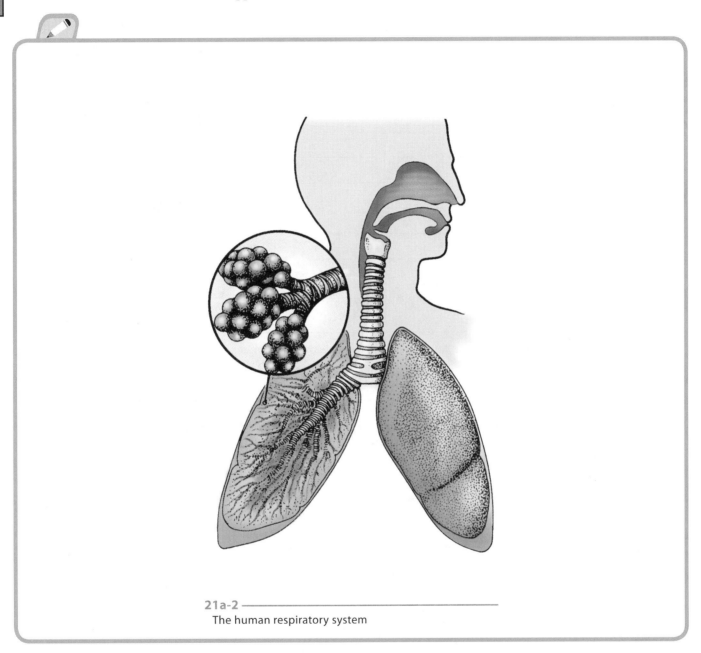

21a-2 —————————————————
The human respiratory system

Listening to Your Lungs

Air rushing into and out of healthy respiratory structures makes various sounds. Many respiratory problems cause various abnormal sounds that a physician can hear using a stethoscope. It is hoped that you will not hear abnormal respiratory sounds when listening to your lab partner's breathing. It can be interesting, however, to listen to normal sounds of the respiratory system.

I. Listen to your partner's lungs.

- Using a tissue and alcohol, clean the earpieces of a stethoscope.

- Place the stethoscope in your ears, allowing the tubes to hang freely and being careful not to hit the diaphragm on hard objects. (The noise can be very loud.)

- Place the diaphragm of the stethoscope on your lab partner's back and press lightly as he breathes normally.
- Listen to a normal breath or two in areas A–F as labeled on Figure 21a-3. Describe the sounds you hear.

_____

_____

_____

_____

_____

_____

_____

_____

_____

_____

21a-3
Areas to place stethoscope

- Are the sounds you hear different in different areas?

_____

- Listen to a deep breath in the same areas. Do you hear a difference?   ☐ yes ☐ no   If so, describe the difference and tell what may account for it.

_____

_____

- Listen to areas A and E while the person coughs. Describe what you hear.

_____

_____

- Listen to areas A and E while the person talks. Describe what you hear.

_____

_____

II. Listen to your partner's throat.
- Listen to your lab partner's breathing by placing the stethoscope in area G.
- Listen to your lab partner's voice in the same area.
- Describe what you hear.

_____

_____

_____

21b The Human Digestive System

Introduction

The first part of this laboratory exercise involves identifying and labeling structures of the human digestive system and completing a chart dealing with human digestion. The last part of the exercise deals with calories, weight gain, and weight loss.

Structures of the Digestive System

R E O

I. Label Figure 21b-1.

- Label as many structures as you can. You should have at least ten structures labeled.

- Under each label indicate what activity of physical digestion happens in that structure. If the structure is not involved in physical digestion, give a brief statement of its function. Enclose this information in parentheses.

Goals

✓ Learn about the structures of the digestive system and the process of digestion in the human body

✓ Learn about calories and weight gain or loss

Materials

calculator (optional)

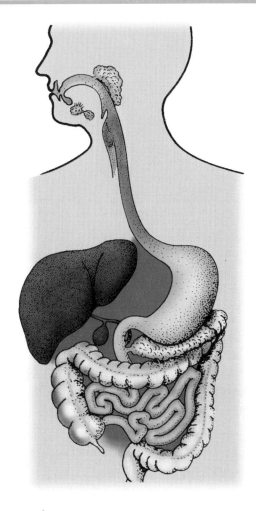

21b-1 —————————————
The human digestive system

II. Fill in the Chemical Digestion chart. If certain foods undergo no chemical digestion in a particular area, draw a line through that space.

Chemical Digestion				
Organs		Starches	Fats	Proteins
Mouth	Enzymes[1]			
	Beginning substances[2]			
	Ending substances[3]			
Stomach	Enzymes			
	Beginning substances			
	Ending substances			
Small intestine	Enzymes			
	Beginning substances			
	Ending substances			

[1]For each row in this chart labeled *Enzymes*, list all the enzymes involved in chemical digestion in the proper spaces, regardless of the sequence in which they work.
[2]For each row labeled *Beginning substances*, list all the substances acted on by any of the enzymes listed.
[3]For each row labeled *Ending substances*, list the substances that result after all the enzymes act on the beginning substances you listed.

🏠 *Calories and Pounds*

Some people think that Calories and pounds are different names for the same thing. This is not true. Calories are units of heat energy; pounds are units of weight. In the human body, however, Calories and pounds are converted from one to the other. It is good to understand the relative proportions of Calories contained in food to pounds of body weight.

There are many factors that could alter the numbers given in the following charts. For example, a person who is in poor physical condition or is overweight will use more calories doing a particular physical activity. Some apples contain more sugar than others and thus would have more calories.

I. Use the figures in the Selected Foods and Calorie Values chart (p. 189) to answer the following questions.

- How many apples would you have to eat to gain a pound of body weight? _____

- How many pats of butter (a pat is 1 T [tablespoon]) would you have to eat to gain a pound of body weight?

    _____

- How many cups of ice cream would you have to eat to gain a pound of body weight? _____

- How many cups of peanuts would you have to eat to gain a pound of body weight? _____

name: _____

Selected Foods and Calorie Values

Food	Calories	Food	Calories
Fruits		**Meats, cont.**	
apple (1 large)	70	chicken, fried (half breast, 3.3 oz)	154
banana (1 large)	85	egg (1)	80
cantaloupe (½)	40	frankfurter (1)	155
orange (1 large)	70	hamburger, on bun (0.25 lb)	416
raisins (1 cup)	460	beef stew (1 cup)	250
strawberries (1 cup)	55	ocean perch, fried (3 oz)	195
watermelon (2 lb slice)	120	**Seeds and Nuts**	
Vegetables		almonds, shelled (1 cup)	850
broccoli (1 cup)	60	peanut butter (1 T)	90
carrots, cooked (1 cup)	45	peanuts, shelled (1 cup)	840
celery stalk (8 in.)	5	**Breads and Cakes**	
cucumber (1 in. slice)	5	angel food cake (2 in. slice)	110
dill pickle (1 large)	15	Boston cream pie (3.3 oz)	329
green peas (1 cup)	110	cheesecake (4 oz)	215
green pepper (1 raw)	15	doughnut, powdered sugar (1.8 oz)	233
onion (1 in. slice)	80	pancake (4 in. diameter)	60
potato, baked (5 oz)	90	pumpkin pie (4 in. section)	265
potatoes, French-fried (2 oz)	200	white bread (1 slice)	62
sweet corn (5 in. ear)	65	**Miscellaneous**	
Dairy Products		chicken soup (1 cup)	75
butter or margarine (1 T)	100	cola (6 oz)	73
cottage cheese (1 oz)	30	French salad dressing (1 T)	90
ice cream (1 cup)	295	fudge (1 oz)	115
whole milk (1 cup)	165	honey (1 T)	60
yogurt (1 cup)	120	ketchup (1 T)	15
Meats		mayonnaise (1 T)	110
beef, roast (3 oz)	265	sugar (1 T)	50

Calories Used for Selected Activities

Activity	Calories per hour	Activity	Calories per hour
watching TV, reading	25	walking (2.5 mph)	210
driving car	50	golfing, lawn mowing	250
eating	50	bowling	270
sewing	50	swimming (0.25 mph)	300
typing	50	volleyball, roller-skating	350
washing dishes	75	table tennis	360
playing piano	75	hiking	400
brushing teeth or hair	100	tennis	420
dusting furniture	150	shoveling	500
mopping floors	200	skiing	600
bicycling (5.5 mph)	210	running (10 mph)	900

II. Use the figures in the Calories Used for Selected Activities chart (p. 189) to answer the following questions.

- How many hours would you have to watch TV to lose a pound of body weight? _____
- How many hours would you have to wash dishes to lose a pound of body weight? _____
- How many hours would you have to walk at 2.5 mph to lose a pound of body weight? _____
- How many hours would you have to play volleyball to lose a pound of body weight? _____
- How many hours would you have to run at 10 mph to lose a pound of body weight? _____

III. Although many factors are involved in weight gain and loss, working the following problems will help you see the relationship between the two. (Indicate whether there is a gain or a loss of weight and how many pounds are involved.)

- One day at breakfast, Tom read that the quantity of cereal he was consuming gave him a breakfast of three hundred calories. He decided that two boiled eggs, two slices of toast with a quarter tablespoon of butter on each, and an orange would be a better breakfast. If Tom kept his other meals the same and did not change his amount of activity, what would be his weight change in one year?

  _____

- At the end of the school year, Maria discovered that her dresses were getting tight. She decided that for the thirteen weeks of summer vacation, she would invest the two hours a day she normally spent doing her school assignments in physical exercise. Maria decided that for six days a week she would spend one hour walking, a half hour in the pool swimming, and a half hour bicycling to and from the pool. If she does not change her food intake, how much weight change can she expect?

  _____

- Jason enjoyed his summer job working five days a week at the bank, but he noticed that for the two summers he had held that job he had gained about twenty pounds in thirteen weeks. He knew that he would do better in soccer if he could keep that weight off. Normally he had two powdered sugar doughnuts at his morning break and another two at the afternoon break. He decided to substitute a cup of yogurt for each of these snacks. If all other factors remain the same, would the amount of weight Jason usually gains change? ☐ yes ☐ no   Explain.

  _____

  _____

  _____

  _____

  _____

  _____

22a Human Blood

Introduction

The blood is a multipurpose tissue in the body. It maintains a steady flow of oxygen to every cell, transports carbon dioxide waste from the cells to the lungs to be expelled, moves hormones to target areas in the body, protects the body when it is invaded by disease-causing microorganisms, and performs many more functions. Blood cells play an essential role in these functions of the blood. Modern science has discovered that blood cells can also provide information for successful transfusions, criminal investigations, and genetic relationships.

Goals

✓ Observe some of the clinically important characteristics of human blood
✓ Analyze the results of a blood typing test
✓ Observe human blood cells

Materials

simulated-blood kit
toothpicks
microscope
preserved slides of human blood

Blood Types

Before a transfusion can be given, the blood must be accurately typed. If the wrong type is transfused, the donated blood may agglutinate in the recipient's body, causing death. Blood is usually typed by testing it with sera. Blood typing serum is made from blood plasma; therefore, it contains only antibodies. Anti-A serum, then, contains anti-A antibodies and will cause type A blood (which contains A antigens) to agglutinate. (See pp. 543–44 of your text.)

I. Answer the following questions regarding blood typing sera, antigens, and antibodies.

- What antigens would be found in anti-B serum? Why?

  _____

- What antibodies would be found in anti-B serum?

  _____

- If the red blood cells agglutinate when anti-A serum is placed on the blood, what blood type(s) are possible for that person?

  _____

- If the red blood cells agglutinate when both anti-A and anti-B sera are placed on the blood, what blood type(s) are possible for that person?

  _____

- If the red blood cells do not agglutinate when either anti-A or anti-B serum is placed on the blood, what blood type(s) are possible for that person?

  _____

- What purpose do antibodies have in the body?

  _____

  _____

II. Blood type is genetically inherited.

- The ABO blood types are an example of multiple alleles. A person can only inherit two alleles, one from each parent, but there are three alleles possible for the gene. There is one allele that codes for the A antigen and one allele that codes for the B antigen. These two alleles are codominant, meaning they will both be expressed if inherited. In addition, there is a recessive allele that codes for neither antigen. (See p. 120 of your text.)

- Answer the following questions regarding the genetics of the ABO blood types.
  - What is the phenotype, or blood type, of a person expressing the codominant trait?

    _____

  - What is the genotype of a person expressing the codominant trait? (See p. 120 of your text for review on how to write the genotypes of blood types.)

    _____

  - What is the phenotype of a person expressing the homozygous recessive trait?

    _____

  - What is the genotype of a person expressing the homozygous recessive trait?

    _____

  - More than one combination of alleles will result in a blood type of A or B. What genotypes are possible for these two blood types?

    _____

III. Solve the following blood typing problem, using the simulated-blood typing kit provided by your teacher.

- The situation
  - Recently, two couples delivered healthy baby girls at a local hospital on the same day. Dan and Sue named their daughter Joy. Andrew and Ann named their little girl Grace. The babies were able to go home with their parents a few days afterwards. Once at home, Ann began to wonder if her child had been switched with the other little girl at the hospital. Baby Grace's hair was red and there was no one with red hair in their family. Ann requested that a blood test be done to determine whether the babies had been switched at the hospital.
  - DNA testing is a more accurate testing method to determine genetic inheritance; however, blood testing can also be done since it is a genetically inherited trait. You will need to determine the blood types of the babies and then compare them with the parents' blood types to determine if it is possible that the babies were switched at the hospital and further testing is needed.

- The data
  - Place two separate drops of synthetic blood from the dropper labeled *Joy, child 1* on a blood typing card. Label one *Drop A* and the other *Drop B*.

    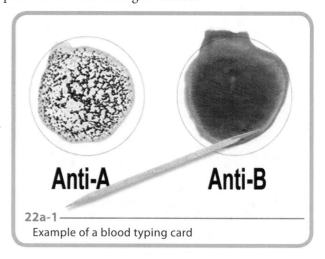

    22a-1
    Example of a blood typing card

    - Without touching the serum dropper to the synthetic blood, place a drop of anti-A serum on top of Drop A. Stir the drop of blood with a toothpick. Does the blood agglutinate? ☐ yes ☐ no
    - Repeat the above operation, using anti-B serum on Drop B and a fresh toothpick. Does the blood agglutinate? ☐ yes ☐ no
    - What type of blood does Joy have?

  - Now place two separate drops of synthetic blood from the dropper labeled *Grace, child 2* on another blood typing card. Label one *Drop A* and the other *Drop B*.
    - Without touching the serum dropper to the synthetic blood, place a drop of anti-A serum on top of Drop A. Stir the drop of blood with a toothpick. Does the blood agglutinate? ☐ yes ☐ no

♦ Repeat the above operation, using anti-B serum on Drop B and a fresh toothpick. Does the blood agglutinate? ☐ yes ☐ no

♦ What type of blood does Grace have?

_____

☐ Record the parents' blood types. (Your teacher either will provide you with the materials to determine the parents' blood types on your own or will give you this information.)

♦ Joy's parents: Dan _____ Sue _____

♦ Grace's parents: Andrew _____ Ann _____

- The conclusion

  ☐ Using Punnett squares and the data listed above, prove whether it is possible that the babies were switched at the hospital.

  ☐ Answer the following questions regarding your conclusions:

  ♦ Is it possible that the babies were switched at the hospital and further testing needs to be done? Explain.

_____

_____

_____

_____

_____

_____

_____

  ♦ If baby Joy's blood type had been type A, would the data have been conclusive? Why or why not?

_____

_____

  ♦ Why can people with Joy's blood type donate blood to anybody? Why are they unable to receive blood from any other blood type? What name is given to people with this blood type?

_____

_____

_____

_____

_____

_____

_____

Observing Blood Cells

I. Observe a preserved slide of blood.

- Be sure to observe a section of the slide where the blood is one cell-layer thick. Such an area usually appears to have nothing on it when you look at it with the unaided eye.

- Observe red blood cells.

- Do you see any atypical shapes? ☐ yes   ☐ no

- What might account for them?

  _____

  _____

- Scan the slide until you find at least three white blood cells. How can you distinguish them from the red blood cells?

  _____

  _____

  _____

II. Draw blood cells in Area A.

- Draw ten red blood cells and at least two white blood cells.

- Label all the features of white blood cells you can identify.

A

22b Human Blood Circulation

Introduction

During almost every physical exam, your pulse rate and your blood pressure will be measured. Many different diseases or disorders can affect pulse rate and blood pressure. By knowing these statistics, a physician can begin to form his diagnosis of his patient's condition. In this laboratory exercise you will find your pulse rate and blood pressure.

Physicians also listen to the sounds of a person's heart. They can determine conditions of the heart by listening to the sounds made by the closing of its valves. An irregular heartbeat is an indication of disease, disorder, or emotional trauma. In this exercise you will listen to the sounds of your heart. You will also count your partner's breathing rate, and he will count his own pulse rate while he engages in various activities. Afterwards you will compare the different rates.

> ### Goals
> ✓ Learn to take a pulse
> ✓ Listen to the heart
> ✓ Learn how blood pressure is measured
> ✓ Compare changes in the pulse rate and the breathing rate

> ### Materials
> stopwatch (or clock with second hand)
> stethoscope
> colored pencils
> tissues
> isopropyl (rubbing) alcohol
> sphygmomanometer

The Pulse and Heart Rates

Pulse and Heart Rates During Rest

I. Take your pulse.

- Determine your pulse by using a stopwatch or a clock with a second hand.

  □ Count the number of pulses that occur in fifteen seconds.

Where to Find Your Pulse

Use one of the two methods described below to find your pulse. Your radial pulse can be monitored by someone else. The carotid pulse is the usual method a person uses to find his own pulse rate. (It is recommended that you learn to take a pulse using both methods.)

The Radial Pulse
- Have your partner sit quietly for about four minutes. (Work on other sections of the lab.)
- While he is seated, find his radial pulse by placing two fingertips (not your thumb) over the area where the radial artery passes over the radius of the wrist.

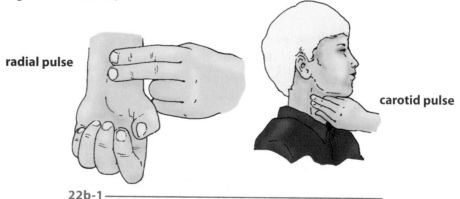

22b-1
Locating radial and carotid pulse

The Carotid Pulse
- Sit quietly for about four minutes. (Work on other sections of the lab.)
- Hold your head so that your jaw is horizontal or slightly elevated.
- Place the anterior (palm) side of your index and middle finger on the side of your neck below the jaw, under the ear, in the area of the carotid artery. Press lightly.

◻ Multiply by four to get the rate per minute. Record the number.

◻ Repeat the procedure two more times and average the results.

- What is your pulse rate while you are seated? _____ beats per minute

II. Listen to your heart.

- While seated, listen to your own heart, following these instructions.

◻ Using a tissue and alcohol, clean the earpieces of a stethoscope.

◻ Place the stethoscope in your ears, allowing the tubes to hang freely.

◻ Place the diaphragm of the stethoscope just below your third rib, slightly to the left of the sternum.

◻ Using a stopwatch or a clock with a second hand, count the number of beats that take place in fifteen seconds. The "lubb-dubb" sound counts as one beat, not two.

◻ Multiply by four to get the rate per minute. Record this number.

◻ Repeat the procedure two more times and average the results.

- What is your seated heart rate? _____ beats per minute

III. Compare your pulse rate and your heart rate.

- Should your pulse rate and your heart rate be the same? ☐ yes   ☐ no

- Explain your answer. _____

_____

Pulse and Breathing Rates During Activity

I. One member of a laboratory group should perform the following physical activities. The data of this one person should be used by everyone in the group to make graphs individually (Section II) and to answer the questions (Section III).

- Sitting

◻ You should already have your subject's seated pulse rate; transfer that information to the box that follows this section.

◻ After your subject has sat quietly for four minutes (working on his lab), count his breathing rate for thirty seconds, and multiply this number by two. Record this information in the box.

- Standing

◻ Have your subject stand quietly (while working on his lab) for three minutes.

◻ Count his breathing for thirty seconds. Multiply the number by two and record the information.

◻ Simultaneously, have him take his pulse for fifteen seconds. Multiply the number by four and record the information.

- Walking

◻ Have your subject walk the distance given by your instructor. As soon as he returns, do the following.

◻ Count his breathing for thirty seconds, multiply the number by two, and record the information.

◻ Simultaneously, have him take his pulse for fifteen seconds. Multiply the number by four and record the information.

- Running

◻ Have your subject run the distance given by your instructor. As soon as he returns, do the following.

◻ Count his breathing for thirty seconds. Multiply the number by two and record the information.

◻ Simultaneously, have him take his pulse for fifteen seconds. Multiply the number by four and record the information.

	Sitting	Standing	Walking	Running
Pulse Rate	_____	_____	_____	_____
Breathing Rate	_____	_____	_____	_____

II. Plot the preceding information on the graph provided, using one color for the pulse rate and another for the breathing rate.

Pulse and Breathing Rates Graph

	Sitting	Standing	Walking	Running
200				
195				
190				
185				
180				
175				
170				
165				
160				
155				
150				
145				
140				
135				
130				
125				
120				
115				
110				
105				
100				
95				
90				
85				
80				
75				
70				
65				
60				
55				
50				
45				
40				
35				
30				
25				
20				
15				
10				
5				
0				

III. Answer the following questions.

- Between which two adjacent activities is there the largest increase in the pulse rate?

  _____

  What explanation can you offer?

  _____

  _____

  _____

- Between which two adjacent activities is there the largest increase in breathing rate?

  _____

  What explanation can you offer?

  _____

  _____

- Would you expect the largest increases in both pulse rate and breathing rate to be between the same two activities? ☐ yes   ☐ no   Why or why not?

  _____

  _____

  _____

- Based on your data, is the largest increase in pulse rate and breathing rate between the same two activities? ☐ yes   ☐ no
  If this is not in keeping with your hypothesis (in the previous question), account for the difference.

  _____

Measuring Your Blood Pressure

Blood pressure is the pressure that the blood exerts against the walls of the arteries. Carefully read the section on blood pressure in your text (p. 553). Although professionals take blood pressure readings quickly and easily, the process is not as easy as it looks. Health-care providers often spend long hours learning the proper techniques. In the first part of this laboratory exercise, you will record only the systolic pressure, which is easy to determine. The second part provides instructions for finding the diastolic blood pressure for those who would like to try.

Taking a Person's Systolic Blood Pressure

I. Set up the sphygmomanometer.

- Place the cuff around your lab partner's arm in the area of the belly of the biceps brachii. It should be snug, but not tight.

- Turn the thumbscrew near the squeeze bulb until the valve is closed.

- Have your lab partner bend his arm and place it palm up on the table.

- Place the stethoscope earpieces in your ears. Be careful not to hit the diaphragm against any object.

- Find your partner's radial pulse with your fingers.

II. Take the systolic blood pressure of your partner.

> **Warning!** The remainder of the exercise must be done within thirty seconds. If you are unable to complete it in thirty seconds, you must release the pressure on the arm and permit the blood to flow freely into the arm for a minute before you try again. **Do not cut off the circulation in the arm for more than thirty seconds.** Also, **do not** flex the arm muscles while the cuff is tight. Such movements can destroy a mercury sphygmomanometer.

- While feeling your partner's radial pulse, squeeze the bulb repeatedly until you can no longer feel a pulse in the radial artery.
  - Keep your eye on the pressure gauge (mercury or dial gauge). The pulse should stop near 140 mm Hg.
  - As soon as the pulse ceases, increase the pressure about twenty points on the scale; then stop squeezing the bulb.
- Place the diaphragm of the stethoscope in the cubital fossa (pit in the bend of the arm).
- Partially release the thumbscrew. You will hear the air hiss out and see the pressure gauge drop.
  - Listen for the sound of the first spurt of blood as it passes through the partially closed artery.

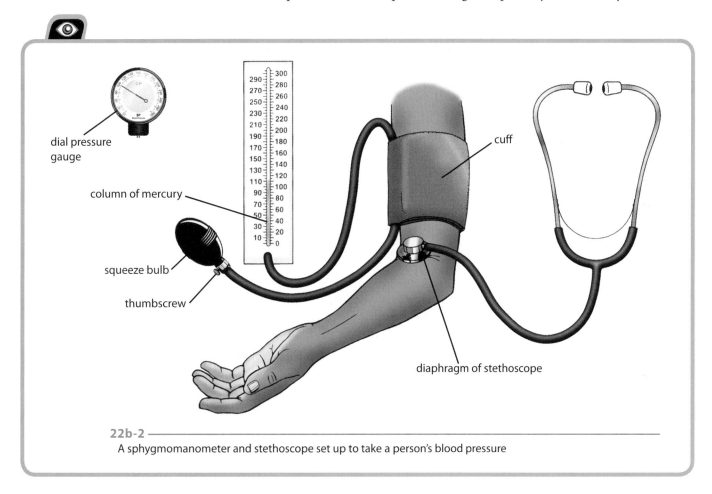

dial pressure gauge

column of mercury

squeeze bulb

thumbscrew

cuff

diaphragm of stethoscope

22b-2
A sphygmomanometer and stethoscope set up to take a person's blood pressure

  - When you first hear the sound, note the number indicated on the pressure gauge. (If it is a mercury gauge, the mercury should take a quick little jump as the sound starts; the needle on a dial gauge will slightly move also.)
- Immediately release the thumbscrew completely. NOTE: If you must repeat the procedure more than three times in order to do it right, switch the cuff to the other arm.

III. Answer the following questions.
- What was the person's systolic blood pressure? _____
- Normal systolic blood pressure for adults is about 120 mm Hg; for young people it is slightly lower. What could cause a higher than normal pressure? (List three possible explanations.)

_____

_____

_____

Taking a Person's Diastolic Blood Pressure

I. Take the diastolic blood pressure of your partner.

- After taking the systolic blood pressure, instead of releasing the thumbscrew rapidly, continue to allow the air to escape slowly.
- Continue listening to the sounds.
    - At one point the sounds will become softer and muffled.
    - At this point the pressure gauge indicates the diastolic blood pressure.

II. Answer the following questions.

- What is your partner's diastolic blood pressure?

  _____

- How would that blood pressure (BP) normally be written?

  _____

- Is your partner's blood pressure normal for his age? ☐ yes   ☐ no

  If not, what may account for the irregularity?

  _____

  _____

23a   Human Reflexes

Introduction

A reflex is considered the lowest level of human behavior because it involves responses that do not involve conscious decision making. In other words, your body performs reflexes without your having to think about them. As you study the reflex arc and various human reflexes, you should come to understand why they are important and how they operate.

The Reflex Arc

Reflexes originate at receptors found in the skin, tendons, muscles, and other body structures. When stimulated, these receptors send impulses over sensory neurons to the central nervous system (CNS). In the CNS, connections are often made through interneurons to motor neurons. As impulses travel over these motor neurons, they cause effectors (muscles) to contract, producing the reflex action. These innate (inborn) behaviors are unlearned, nearly instantaneous reactions to a single, simple stimulus.

Materials

reflex mallet
penlight

Demonstrating the Patellar (Knee-Jerk) Reflex

I.   Sit comfortably in a chair and cross your legs above the knees, or sit on a high surface so that your feet do not touch the floor. Keep the thigh of your leg relaxed.

II. Have your lab partner tap your patellar tendon just below the patella with the reflex mallet. Do not watch as the tendon is struck. What is the reaction?

_____

III. Try variations of the patellar reflex.

- Try to stiffen your bent leg so that the reflex will not work. Is it possible to tense the leg so much that the reflex will not work? ☐ yes   ☐ no

- Try the patellar reflex with the leg at different degrees of straightness (with the knee at different angles).

   □ Does this affect the strength of the reflex? ☐ yes   ☐ no

   □ Does the reflex get weaker or stronger as the knee is straightened? ☐ weaker   ☐ stronger

Studying a Reflex Arc

I.   Label the following terms on Figure 23a-1: receptors of sensory neuron, sensory neuron, dendrites of sensory neuron, axon of sensory neuron, central nervous system, interneuron, motor neuron, axon of motor neuron, and effector.

II. A doctor tests reflexes for several reasons. List at least two.

_____

_____

_____

_____

_____

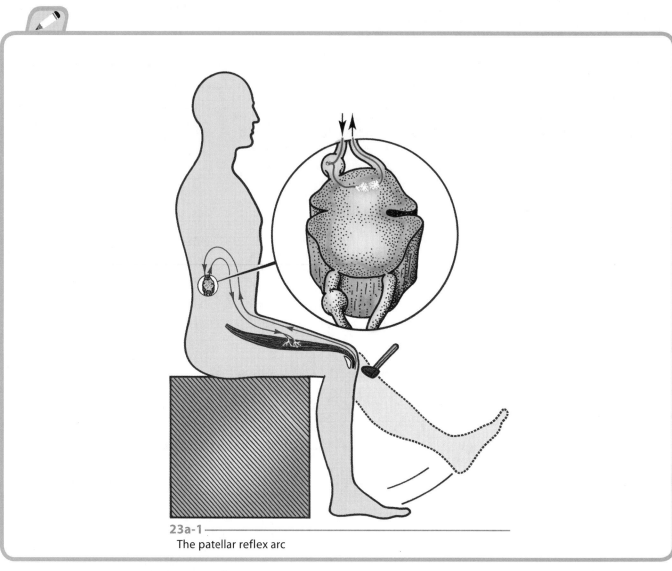

23a-1
The patellar reflex arc

Demonstrating Other Human Reflexes

I. The Achilles (ankle-jerk) reflex

- Have your partner kneel on a chair with his feet hanging over the edge.
- Tap his Achilles tendon with the blunt end of the reflex mallet.
- Describe the reflex action. _____

_____

II. The pupillary reflex

- In a dimly lit area, shine the beam of a penlight into your partner's right eye, being careful not to shine the beam into the left eye.
- What happens to the pupil of the right eye? _____
- What happens to the pupil of the left eye? _____
- Try the experiment again, shining the beam into the left eye this time. Are the results the same?
  ☐ yes ☐ no If not, why not?

_____

_____

23b   Minor Senses in Humans

Introduction

Although called the minor senses, taste, smell, balance, and touch (including pressure, pain, and temperature sensations) are all important to your well-being. Because these senses are often thought of as being less important than sight and hearing, they are often taken for granted. But if one of these senses is not working properly, a person is handicapped. In this exercise you will test some of these not-so-minor senses.

The Senses of Taste and Smell

Two closely allied senses are the senses of taste and smell. Having a cold shows you that many of the tastes you enjoy are actually smells. Try these experiments to determine some of the relationships between taste and smell.

The Taste and Smell of Sugar

I. Smell a sugar cube.

  - Describe the smell.

    _____

  - Based on the smell, what would you expect sugar to taste like?

    _____

    _____

II. Taste a sugar cube.

  - Rinse your mouth with clean water.
  - Stick your tongue out and dry it with a paper towel.
  - Place a sugar cube on the center of your dry tongue. Do not pull your tongue back into your mouth.
  - Record the time it takes for you to taste the sugar. _____ seconds
  - Remove the sugar cube as soon as you taste it.
  - Rinse your mouth with clean water.
  - Stick your tongue out and wet it with clean water.
  - Place the opposite side of the same sugar cube on the same area of your tongue. Do not pull your tongue back into your mouth.
  - Record the time it takes for you to taste the sugar. _____ seconds
  - Explain the differences in time it took to taste the sugar.

    _____

    _____

    _____

The Taste and Smell of Vanilla

I. Smell the vanilla extract and then describe the smell.

    _____

II. Dip a cotton swab into some vanilla extract and touch the swab to your tongue. (You may need to touch it to several areas of the tongue.) Describe the taste.

_____

- Does vanilla extract taste the way it smells? ☐ yes   ☐ no
- Which sense do you think accounts for the taste we normally call vanilla (such as in vanilla ice cream and vanilla pudding)?

_____

Sensation of Heat and Cold on the Skin

Your skin receives numerous sensations. Your sense of touch involves only one set of nerves. Pain, temperature, and pressure (and possibly other sensations) are perceived by other nerve endings in the skin. In this exercise you are asked to determine whether heat and cold are different sensations of the same nerve or are the sensations of two different nerves.

Write your hypothesis:

_____

_____

_____

R E O

Sensing Hot and Cold

I. Obtain a beaker of hot water and place a blunt metal or glass rod in it. Make sure that the water is not hot enough to burn the skin. Also obtain a beaker of ice water and place a similar rod in it.

II. Test your partner's sense of hot or cold.

- With a washable-ink pen, place six small dots on the back of your partner's hand separated by at least 1.0 cm. On paper, diagram the hand, draw in the dots, and assign each dot a letter.
- Blindfold your partner.
- Randomly place either the hot or cold rod on each of the six dots until every dot has been tested twice for hot and twice for cold.
  - ▫ Quickly dry the rod before placing it on the dot.
  - ▫ Touch the rods with the same pressure to the skin.
  - ▫ Leave the rods in contact with the skin for three seconds, after which your partner must identify whether the rod was hot or cold.
  - ▫ Return the rods to the proper beaker between tests to keep them at the proper temperature.
  - ▫ Record the number of correct and incorrect responses for both hot and cold for each dot.

III. Answer the following questions.

- Which was your partner more often correct in sensing? ☐ hot   ☐ cold
- Was each of the dots equally sensitive to hot and cold, or were some dots easier to identify as hot or cold?

_____

  - ▫ If different areas were sensitive to different temperatures, what would this result suggest?

_____

_____

□ If all areas were equally sensitive to different temperatures, what would this result suggest?

_____

_____

Plotting the Sensation of Heat and Cold

I. With a washable-ink pen, mark a one-inch square on the back of your partner's hand and then draw a 6 × 6 grid in the square. (See the boxes below.)

Cold

Heat

II. Use the hot and cold rods as described above.

- Test all of the areas within the square with the cold probe. Locate and mark on the diagram all the areas that were sensitive to the cold probe.

- Test all of the areas within the square with the hot probe. Locate and mark on the diagram all the areas that were sensitive to the hot probe.

III. According to your experiment, are heat and cold receptors in identical locations on the hand? ☐ yes ☐ no From this fact, what can you conclude about temperature receptors?

_____

The Sense of Balance

Your inner ear contains the delicate structures responsible for the sense of balance. These structures are dependent on the properties of fluids. Moving fluids are used to send the information necessary for your brain to know your position and movements. Your sense of balance is usually quite accurate; however, under certain circumstances the inner ear fluids can send impulses to your brain that do not reflect reality.

I. Test normal visual and motor coordination.

- Have your partner sit cross-legged in a swivel chair.

- Place your extended index finger about twenty inches in front of his chest and test his ability to touch your finger.

   □ Have him raise his arm above his head.

   □ Have him extend his index finger and quickly drop his arm until his finger comes into contact with yours. Did his finger make contact on the first try? ☐ yes ☐ no

   □ Repeat this experiment eight times. Record the number correct. _____

- Have your partner repeat the experiment with his eyes closed.

   □ Did his finger make contact? ☐ yes ☐ no
   If not, by how much did he miss? _____

   □ Repeat this experiment eight times. Record the number correct. _____

II. Test visual and motor coordination after movement.

- While your partner has his eyes open, twirl him rapidly in the chair for fifteen seconds.

   □ Stop him abruptly and have him try the finger-touching experiment.

   □ How many tries did it take for him to make contact as well as he did before twirling? _____

- When he is no longer dizzy, have him close his eyes and again twirl him rapidly in the chair for fifteen seconds.
  - He should then open his eyes, note where your finger is, close his eyes, raise his hand above his head, and try to make contact.
  - How many tries did it take for him to make contact as well as he did before twirling? _____
- When he is no longer dizzy, repeat the twirling-chair test with his eyes closed.
  - This time have him keep his eyes open as he tries to touch your finger.
  - How many tries did it take him to make contact as well as he did before twirling? _____

III. Answer the following questions. (Some may require careful reasoning.)

- When did he perform better? ☐ before being twirled   ☐ after being twirled

  Explain your answer, telling what structures are responsible.

  _____

  _____

  _____

  _____

- Compared to performing the experiment without twirling and with eyes open, how difficult would it be to perform the following actions?
  - Without twirling and with eyes closed while he tries to make contact

    _____

  - With eyes open while he twirls and with eyes open while he tries to make contact

    _____

  - With eyes closed while he twirls and with eyes closed while he tries to make contact

    _____

  - With eyes closed while he twirls and with eyes open while he tries to make contact

    _____

- What would account for these differences in difficulty?

  _____

  _____

  _____

  _____

23c   The Human Eye and Ear

Introduction

A minor shortcoming of a person's vision or hearing may go unnoticed for years. For example, astigmatism in one eye may be compensated for by the other eye so that a person may not be aware that he has blurred vision. Some people who have red-green colorblindness (one of the most common forms of colorblindness) do not realize it until they are adults. In this exercise you will perform some simple tests on your eyes and ears.

> **Goals**
>
> ✓ Perform some simple vision and hearing tests
>
> ✓ Note the clinical value of such tests to a physician

The Eye and Sight

Vision is one of the senses on which humans rely most. It is also more prone to minor disorders than are other senses. In the following exercises, you will perform some simple tests on your vision (or your lab partner's vision).

> **Materials**
>
> Snellen eye chart
>
> tape measure
>
> penlight
>
> red and green cellophane
>
> white paper
>
> Holmgren color vision test
>
> tuning forks of assorted frequencies (including 128 and 256 cps)

Structures of the Eye

I. Examine your partner's eye (or use a mirror to examine your own eye) and identify the following structures. Give definitions where required.

- Lids: _____
- Conjunctiva: the lining of the eyelid and transparent covering of the anterior eyeball, except the cornea
- Openings of nasolacrimal ducts: openings of the tubes (ducts) that carry tears from the eyes into the nose
- Cornea: _____
- Sclera: _____
- Iris: _____
- Pupil: _____

II. Label as many structures of the eye as possible on Figure 23c-1.

Snellen Test for Visual Acuity

A person's visual acuity (visual sharpness) can be tested with a Snellen eye chart, which consists of rows of black letters of different sizes printed on a white card. The distance from which those letters can be read by the normal eye is printed beside each line of letters.

I. Check your visual acuity by doing the following:

- Remove glasses if you wear them. (If possible, remove contact lenses.)
- Stand twenty feet from the chart and cover your left eye with your hand. (Keep the covered eye open.)
- Have your lab partner point out the line of letters that is marked "20 ft." Read the lines as your partner checks to see if you are correct.

  □ If you are able to read the line marked "20 ft," try the next smaller line. Continue until you can no longer read most of the letters accurately.

  □ If you cannot read the line marked "20 ft," have your partner point to the line with the next larger size of type, and so on, until you can read accurately most of the letters on the line that he indicates. (Your partner should point out the letters in the line at random so that you do not memorize the order of the letters.)

  □ Note the number by the last line that you are able to read accurately.

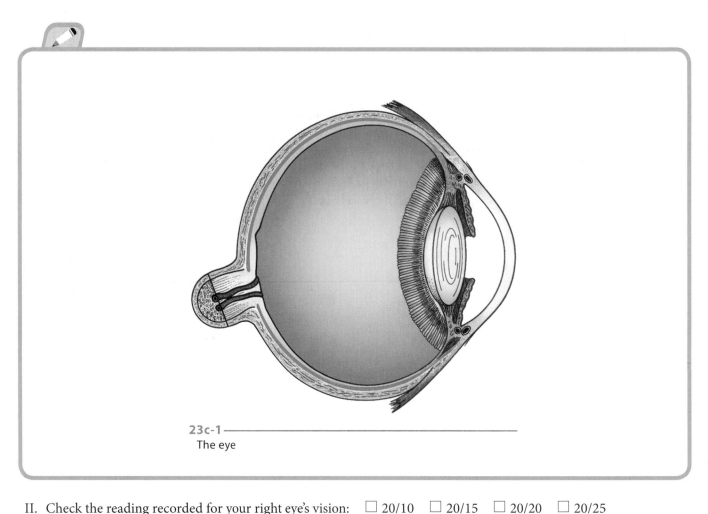

23c-1 ───────────────────────────
The eye

II. Check the reading recorded for your right eye's vision: ☐ 20/10 ☐ 20/15 ☐ 20/20 ☐ 20/25 ☐ 20/30 ☐ 20/40 ☐ 20/50 ☐ 20/70 ☐ 20/100 ☐ 20/200.

III. Repeat this test, covering your right eye to test your left eye's vision. Check the reading recorded for your left eye's vision: ☐ 20/10 ☐ 20/15 ☐ 20/20 ☐ 20/25 ☐ 20/30 ☐ 20/40 ☐ 20/50 ☐ 20/70 ☐ 20/100 ☐ 20/200.

Testing for Astigmatism

R **E** **O**

I. Define *astigmatism*.

_____

II. Check yourself for astigmatism.

- Cover your left eye and hold the diagram for testing astigmatism (Figure 23c-2) about six inches in front of your right eye.

- Look directly into the center of the empty circle of the diagram. Be sure your pupil is directly over the central white area.

- If any of the lines appear blurred, you probably have astigmatism in the corresponding area of your right eye.

- Do you have astigmatism in your right eye? ☐ yes ☐ no If so, in which areas (indicated by numbers at ends of lines)? _____

- Repeat the procedure, covering the right eye and observing with the left eye.

- Do you have astigmatism in your left eye? ☐ yes ☐ no If so, in which areas? _____

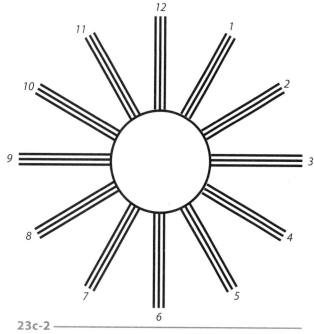

23c-2
Test for astigmatism

Demonstration of the Blind Spot

I.   Read about the blind spot on page 583 of your text.

II. Find your blind spot by using Figure 23c-3.

- Position the diagram so that the dot is to the right of the plus sign.

- Hold the diagram about eighteen inches from your eye, with the plus sign directly in front of your right eye. Cover your left eye.

- Move the diagram slowly toward you as you stare at the plus sign. At a certain point the dot will disappear. The dot is then in your blind spot.

- Have your partner measure the distance from your eye to the paper. What is the distance?

  _____

- Repeat for your left eye. With the dot to the left of the plus sign, place the plus sign directly in front of your left eye and cover your right eye. At what distance does the dot disappear?

  _____

III. What effect would the blind spot have on a person who has only one eye? Should such a person be allowed to drive? ☐ yes ☐ no   Why or why not?

_____

_____

_____

23c-3
Blind spot test

Visual Accommodation

R E O I. Read about visual accommodation on page 583 in your text.

II. Demonstrate visual accommodation.

- Have your partner look at an object across the room while you hold a pencil about eighteen inches in front of his nose. Then ask him to look at the pencil.

- What was the change in the size of the pupils? _____

- Did his eyes move in any other way? ☐ yes   ☐ no

  If so, how? _____

III. Demonstrate near-point accommodation.

- Another important part of accommodation is near-point accommodation. The near point is the closest distance at which sharp focus is attained.

- Determine the near point of your eyes by covering your left eye and focusing with your right eye on the *D* at the beginning of this sentence.

  □ Move this page toward your right eye until the letter no longer appears sharp and clear.

  □ Move the page away until the letter is clear again.

  □ Have your partner measure the distance from the page to your eye.

- Repeat the process for the left eye.

- Record your near-point accommodation distance.

  Left eye: _____   Right eye: _____

- The near-point accommodation distance increases with age because the lens of the eye loses its elasticity.

  □ Is your near-point accommodation distance normal for your age? ☐ yes   ☐ no

  □ When a person can no longer focus on the print of a book at a "comfortable" distance (about 20 in.), he needs reading glasses. Based on your present near-point accommodation distance, at what age should you expect to need reading glasses? _____ years old

Average Near-Point Accommodation by Age

Age	Distance in inches
15	3.5
25	4.5
35	6.8
45	20.5
55	33.0

Afterimages

R E O I. An afterimage is the image that a person sees after he stops looking at an object. Such images are most common after looking at an object that is in sharp contrast to its background.

- A positive afterimage is one that is the same color as the object observed.

- A negative afterimage is the complementary color. Negative afterimages are caused by bleaching (fatigue of visual pigments).

II. Observe afterimages.

- Sit in a darkened area.

- Flash a penlight into one eye for not more than one second. Then close your eyes. Is the afterimage positive or negative? ☐ positive   ☐ negative

- Holding a piece of red cellophane between the light and the eye, flash a penlight into one eye for not more than one second. Then close your eyes. Is the afterimage positive or negative? ☐ positive   ☐ negative

- Repeat this test, using a piece of green cellophane. Is the afterimage positive or negative? ☐ positive   ☐ negative

- Shine a penlight steadily into one eye for about twenty seconds and then quickly look at a piece of white paper. (Blinking your eyes will help the appearance of the afterimage.) Is the afterimage positive or negative? ☐ positive ☐ negative

- Holding a piece of red cellophane between the light and your eye, repeat this test. Is the afterimage positive or negative? ☐ positive ☐ negative

- Repeat this test, using a piece of green cellophane. Is the afterimage positive or negative? ☐ positive ☐ negative

Testing for Colorblindness

The Holmgren color vision test consists of a set of colored wool strands that matches a set of mounted wool strands. NOTE: More specific and more accurate tests must be taken to determine colorblindness accurately. The Holmgren test merely indicates that other tests may be necessary. Even a very poor performance on the Holmgren test may not mean that a person is colorblind.

I. Ask your partner to match the loose strands with the mounted ones as rapidly as possible.

II. Note any of the following reactions in your partner:

- Hesitation before placing a colored strand by the one it matches

- Comparisons (laying a strand beside various mounted threads to determine which one it matches)

- Mistakes (whether or not they are corrected)

III. If your partner shows any of these reactions, note which colors caused the problems. Did your partner show colorblindness tendency? ☐ yes ☐ no If so, in what color range? _____

Hearing

You depend greatly on your sense of hearing. The ear plays a vital role in sound perception. Your ears tell you more than just the kind and volume of sound, as some of these experiments will demonstrate.

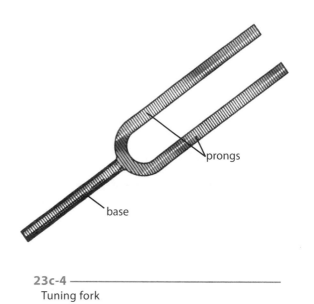

How to Use a Tuning Fork

The tuning fork is an instrument used to produce a specific pitch. This instrument can be used to test for possible hearing problems. You will use it in the next few experiments. A tuning fork consists of a base and a forked pair of prongs. The base supports the prongs, allowing them to vibrate and produce sound when they are struck.

There are two things to remember when using a tuning fork:

- Hold it at its base only. Touching the fork along the prongs stops their vibrating and thus stops the sound. (This may be done after you complete an experiment.)

- Strike the fork against only the palm of your hand or your thigh. Do not strike it on any hard surface since resulting dents may alter its frequency.

prongs

base

23c-4
Tuning fork

Testing Your Hearing

R E O

I. Localizing sound

- Sit in a quiet room with your eyes closed.

- Your partner will strike the fork on his hand and hold it eight to ten inches away from the sides, top, and then back of your head.

- As he moves the fork to different positions around your head, point to the direction from which the sound is coming.

- Your partner may need to strike the tuning fork each time he moves it.

- Were you able to locate sound near the sides of your head? ☐ yes ☐ no Back of your head? ☐ yes ☐ no Top of your head? ☐ yes ☐ no

- Place your index finger over the opening of one of your ears and repeat the experiment.

  Was there any change in the results? ☐ yes ☐ no

  Why or why not?

  _____

  _____

R E O

II. Bone conduction

- Conduction of sound through the skull

  - Sit quietly and plug both ears with your fingers.

  - Your partner will strike the tuning fork and rest the base of the fork on the top of your head.

  - Signal by a slight movement of your head when you hear the fork.

  - Your partner will remove the fork. Can you still hear the sound? ☐ yes ☐ no

  - Your partner will immediately replace the tuning fork on your head. Can you hear the sound? ☐ yes ☐ no

- Conduction of sound through the teeth

  - Sit quietly and plug both ears with your fingers.

  - Your partner will rinse and dry both the tuning fork and his hands. He will strike the fork and place its base (not the vibrating prongs) between your teeth. Only the teeth should come into contact with the tuning fork. (Your lips should not touch it.) Can you hear the sound? ☐ yes ☐ no

  - Remove the fork and wipe it dry.

  - Is there any difference between the sounds heard through the skull and through the teeth? ☐ yes ☐ no If so, how did the sounds differ?

    _____

    _____

- Conduction of sound through the temple

  - Sit quietly and plug both ears with your fingers.

  - Your partner will strike the tuning fork and place its base against your right temple. Do you hear the sound? ☐ yes ☐ no

  - Now repeat the test on the left temple. Do you hear the sound? ☐ yes ☐ no

  - Was there any major difference between what you heard when the right temple was tested and what you heard when the left was tested? ☐ yes ☐ no If yes, give the probable reason.

    _____

    _____

Testing for Deafness

Deafness can result when structures malfunction in any of three different areas: within the parts of the ear that conduct the sound waves (eardrum, ossicles, and other structures), within the nerves and sensory cells of the inner ear, or within the central nervous system. Often conductive deafness affects only one ear. This unilateral (one-sided) sound-conduction deafness is caused by a blockage of sound waves. A person is said to have acoustic nerve deafness if he cannot hear because of problems in his inner ear.

I. Test for unilateral sound-conduction deafness.

- While you sit quietly, your partner will strike a 128 or 256 cps tuning fork and carefully place the base of the fork on the center of your forehead.

- Where does the sound seem loudest? ☐ right   ☐ center   ☐ left

- If you hear the sound better in the left ear or the right ear, you may have conductive deafness. This type of deafness eliminates the background noise that a normal ear hears. Because there is less surrounding noise to distract a sound-conduction deaf ear, the sound heard from the tuning fork on the skull registers more volume in that ear.

  □ Is there a tendency toward sound-conduction deafness in your right ear? ☐ yes   ☐ no

  □ Is there a tendency toward sound-conduction deafness in your left ear? ☐ yes   ☐ no

- What can correct unilateral sound-conduction deafness?

  _____

II. Test for acoustic nerve deafness.

- While you sit quietly, your partner will strike a 128 or 256 cps tuning fork and carefully place the base of the fork on the center of your forehead.

- Plug your right ear. In which ear is the sound louder? ☐ right   ☐ left   ☐ no difference

- Repeat the experiment, this time plugging the left ear. In which ear is the sound louder? ☐ right   ☐ left   ☐ no difference

- Sound conducted through the skull is naturally transmitted better (more loudly) to a plugged ear than to an open ear. If the sound is louder in the unplugged ear, some difficulty other than conduction must be causing the problem. Therefore, if the right ear is plugged and the sound is heard better in the left ear, there may be nerve deafness on the right side.

  □ Is there any tendency toward acoustic nerve deafness in your right ear? ☐ yes   ☐ no

  □ Is there any tendency toward acoustic nerve deafness in your left ear? ☐ yes   ☐ no

- What can be done for acoustic nerve deafness?

  _____

  _____

24 Drugs in Our Culture

Introduction

According to many people, the abuse of psychoactive drugs is one of the major problems faced by our culture. These drugs begin with mental effects, but soon they physically affect the one who takes them. In many cases these drugs leave mental, emotional, and physical scars that may trouble the user for the rest of his life even if he quits using them. The drug abuse also affects his family and his friends in different, often serious, and always harmful ways.

The economic effect of drugs on our society involves not only the money exchanged on the black market but also the millions spent on law enforcement and public and private rehabilitation. It is estimated that the yearly cost of the productivity lost to drugs in the workplace is in the hundreds of millions of dollars.

In this exercise you (or a group of students, if your class does this exercise as a group project) will select or be assigned a drug to research. Only when you know about psychoactive drugs and their effects can you make intelligent decisions about drug-related concerns in our society. It may be easy for you to decide not to be involved with drugs. But since drugs pervade our society, you will need to make decisions regarding everything from the spending of public money to counseling friends regarding their position on drugs and drug-related issues. This project is designed to help you become ready to face these problems.

> ### Goals
> ✓ Learn about the physical effects of various psychoactive drugs
> ✓ Learn about the effects of psychoactive drugs in our culture

> ### Materials
> library or Internet access

Assignment

I. Select a drug (or a group of drugs) and research the effects of the drug.

- Check the following sources for information about the drug.

  □ Go to your local library to locate books that contain information about the drug. Read those parts that contain pertinent information.

  □ Consult the *Reader's Guide to Periodical Literature* for the past several years to find articles containing information about the drug. Read those that contain pertinent information.

  □ Perform an Internet search for the drug. Use reliable sources such as law enforcement agencies; federal, state, or local government sites; and educational sites. Avoid unofficial or unregulated sites.

  □ Information regarding drugs and their use is frequently available from physicians, hospitals, pharmacists, law enforcement authorities, drug rehabilitation centers, and government agencies responsible for drug education. Consult these or other similar sources regarding material about the drug.

- Try to find the following information about the drug. Be more specific than the information found in your textbook.

  □ Briefly describe the history of the drug. Who first used it? Where? When was it introduced into the modern drug culture?

  □ List the physical symptoms caused by the drug. Distinguish between long-term and short-term effects and between effects experienced by "casual users" and "heavy users."

  □ List the drug's mental/emotional effects that cause people to want to take it. Describe these effects on both "casual users" and "heavy users."

  □ How is the drug taken? What problems does a person who uses this drug encounter because of the way it is taken?

  □ What is the source of the drug (synthetic, a foreign country, etc.)? How difficult is it to produce/refine?

- Are there international difficulties (problems between governments) because of the illegal trade of this drug? How extensive are they?

- How much is spent by government agencies (federal, state, local) to control the supply of this drug? How effective is the control? Is there a short supply of the drug because of these control efforts?

- What kinds (groups) of people use this drug (level of education, age, economic group, etc.)? How often do people use this drug, and how much of this drug do the different groups use?

- What kinds of drug education programs are aimed at people not using this drug? What kinds of drug education programs are aimed at people using this drug? Are the drug education programs considered effective?

- Approximately how many people use (or are addicted to) the drug in the United States? In your state? In a nearby major city?

- How much does the drug cost ("street price") for a single dose? To support a "casual" or mild habit? To support a major addiction?

- What kind of drug rehabilitation is offered for abusers of this drug? How much does this rehabilitation cost for one person? How effective is it? Who pays for this rehabilitation?

- Does this drug have legitimate medical uses? What are they? What measures do physicians take to make sure their patients do not abuse this drug?

II. Prepare a report about the information you find.

- Prepare a written report.
    - Write a three- to five-page report on the drug you researched.
        - The introduction and conclusion of your report should be in paragraph form.
        - The main part of your report can be in paragraph form, or it can be in the form of a list of statements answering the questions asked above.
    - Include a complete bibliography of the sources from which you obtained information.

- Prepare an oral report.
    - Prepare a four- to seven-minute oral report on the drug you researched.
    - Cover as many of the questions presented above as possible.
    - Be sure to include references to any source other than printed sources from which you obtained information. (In other words, you do not need to tell about library research sources, but if you talked to someone about this material, you should mention him as part of your report.)
    - Present material you think would be interesting and valuable to the class.

25 Chicken Embryology

Introduction

Embryology is the study of the process through which a single cell grows, divides, and gives rise to thousands of individual cells of many different types. In a relatively short time, these individual cells are able to work together to sustain life. Embryology is a fascinating study, and researchers are working hard to understand the process by which cells with an identical genetic makeup can differentiate to form various tissues such as bone, muscle, liver, thyroid gland, and cartilage. There is also intense research about how cells develop in the right places so that they all fit together in a workable, complete organism. The embryo is too tiny for general observation, and any experimentation greatly affects it. The intricate chemical messengers that turn genes on and off to cause cellular differentiation are of great importance in embryology as well as biotechnology. This laboratory exercise will look at several stages of the embryological growth of a chicken egg in an attempt to observe some of these marvels.

Opening a Chicken Egg

Eggs Incubated Three to Nine Days

I. Without rolling the egg, take it from the incubator. The embryo should be on top of the yolk. If you cut and remove the top part of the shell, you should be able to find the embryo without having to rotate the yolk.

Goals

✓ Observe chicken embryos at different stages of development

✓ Compare the embryonic growth rate of different structures

✓ Learn about various embryonic structures

Materials

fertilized chicken eggs
incubator
scissors
pipet
shallow dishes (finger bowls or large culture dishes)
forceps
physiological saline
scalpel

Incubating Chicken Eggs

Fresh fertilized eggs can be kept at a cool room temperature without incubation for several days. This lowered temperature temporarily stops the embryo's development. Then, when the eggs are placed in an incubator set at 38 °C (100 °F), embryonic growth starts again. If incubated for twenty-one days, normal fertilized chicken eggs will hatch.

Before the laboratory period begins, eggs should be placed in an incubator at intervals so that on the appointed day the egg will have been incubated the proper amount of time. For this exercise, about four different embryonic stages are recommended. Eggs incubated four, nine, twelve, and fourteen days would be ideal. For large classes, however, eggs incubated three, six, nine, twelve, fifteen, and eighteen days could be used.

Several eggs should be incubated for each time period desired so that if one is infertile or if an accident should happen, there are still other eggs to observe. With a pencil, mark on each egg the date and time that its incubation began. Twice a day during the incubation period, the eggs should be turned over so that the chick embryos do not become attached to their shell. A shallow pan of water should be kept in the incubator so that the eggs do not dehydrate.

The class should be divided into groups, with each group responsible for opening an egg of a different age. As each egg is opened, each student should observe the egg and record his observations in the proper spaces on page 220.

II. With the egg lying on its side, draw an oval on the egg as illustrated in Figure 25-1.

III. Carefully insert the point of a pair of scissors a short distance through the shell and cut cautiously around the oval.

IV. Using forceps, remove the loose piece of shell and locate the embryo.

- If the embryo is not visible, use forceps to grasp the chalaza (see the diagram on p. 434 of your text) and rotate the yolk.

- Remove some albumen with a pipet to see the embryo more easily.

- With eggs incubated three to nine days, you will need to cut the amnion to see the embryo clearly. Be sure the other students see these membranes before you cut them.

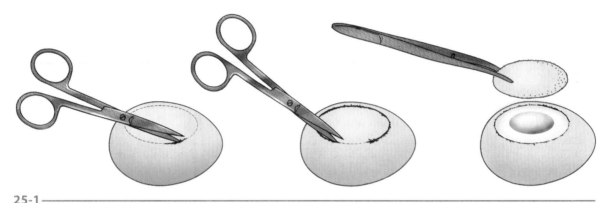

25-1

Opening an egg incubated fewer than ten days

Eggs Incubated Ten Days or More

I. Obtain the eggs from the incubator.

II. Tap the large end of the egg with the handle of a pair of scissors or a scalpel to crack the shell. (See Figure 25-2.)

III. Using forceps, pick away the shell, being careful not to break the shell membrane.

- After a portion of the shell has been removed, place the egg in a shallow dish of physiological saline.

- Continue picking off the shell until it is completely removed.

IV. After observations have been made with the shell membrane intact, break the shell membrane and observe the structures inside.

V. Various membranes will need to be cut before the embryo is clearly visible. Be sure the other students in the class see the membranes before you cut them.

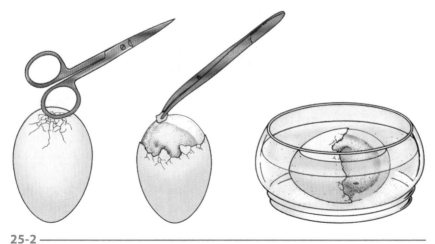

25-2

Opening an egg incubated ten days or more

Observing a Chicken Embryo

I. Look for these structures as you observe.

- **Yolk and yolk sac.** The yolk is the stored food for the embryo. Blood vessels formed by the embryo grow to encircle the yolk sac. As the yolk is used, the yolk sac decreases in size. See pages 418 and 434 of the text.

- **Shell membrane.** The shell membrane is just inside the eggshell and surrounds the albumen (egg white).

- **Amnion and amniotic fluid.** See page 418 of the text.

- **Allantois.** See page 418 of the text.

- **Somites.** Somites are lumps of tissue along the back of the young embryo. These structures develop into the vertebrae, ribs, and muscles of the chicken's body. The column of somites extends beyond the area of the arm and leg buds. But as the body grows, the arm and leg buds appear to move to their proper positions.

- **Blood, heart, and blood vessels.** Blood is one of the first obvious tissues formed by the embryo. The heart is one of the first organs formed. It begins as a pumping tube, which then twists back on itself and becomes a four-chambered pumping organ. At first it is outside the body, but later it is enclosed inside the body cavity. Visible blood vessels go to various egg structures to accomplish different functions.

- **Brain and spinal cord.** The heads of embryos are generally large in comparison to their bodies. The spinal cord is one of the first organs to be recognizable.

- **Limbs.** Starting as bumps on the sides of the body, the limbs slowly take form. Feathers, claws, and scales form before the chick hatches.

- **Eyes and ears.** The eyes form early in embryonic development. They are complex organs that must be fully functional when the chick is hatched. Eyelids form after the eyes do and then grow closed over the eyes. The ear openings can be found along the neck.

- **Mouth and beak.** The mouth begins as an opening to a hollow tube. The tube becomes the alimentary canal. In time, the opening of the tube becomes a mouth and then develops a beak and an egg tooth. The egg tooth is a structure that the chick uses to break the shell when it hatches.

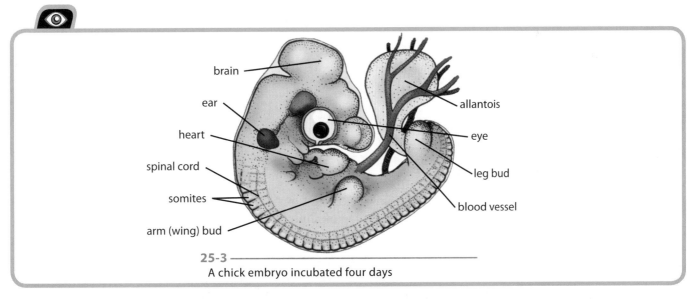

25-3 — A chick embryo incubated four days

II. Record your observations on the Chicken Embryo Development chart.

- Read the summary (p. 220) to find out what types of observations you need to make.

- Be sure that you observe all the eggs when they are first opened and record any observations you may have at that time.

  □ Observe the embryos when they have been removed from their protective membranes.

  □ In the spaces provided on the Chicken Embryo Development chart, describe extensively the development of each of the structures listed. Use additional paper if necessary.

Chicken Embryo Development						
Structures	___ Days	___ Days	___ Days	___ Days	___ Days	___ Days
yolk and yolk sac						
amnion and amniotic fluid						
allantois						
somites						
blood, heart, and blood vessels						
brain and spinal cord						
limbs						
eyes						
ears						
mouth and beak						

🏠 Writing a Summary

I. Prepare a report (one to two pages) discussing the changes in the yolk, yolk sac, amnion, amniotic fluid, and allantois of the chicken eggs you observed. Keeping in mind the functions of these structures, give probable reasons for the changes you observed.

II. Prepare a report (one to two pages) discussing the development of the heart, blood, blood vessels, brain, spinal cord, and somites of the chicken embryos you observed. Describe their changes as the embryo becomes larger. Keeping in mind the function of each of these structures in the adult chicken, give probable reasons for the different rates of growth you observed.

III. Prepare a report (one to two pages) discussing the relative developments of the front and back limbs, eyes, ears, mouth, and beak of the chicken embryos you observed. Keeping in mind what a chick has to do as soon as it is hatched, explain why the sequence of development in each of these structures is logical.

Laboratory Final Examination: The Rat

Introduction

The Rat Lab (as this laboratory final examination will be called) will serve as a final test of your laboratory skills. The value of this lab will be one hundred twenty points. These points will be earned through written quizzes and the demonstration of laboratory skills. This laboratory exercise has no blanks to fill in, no drawings to make, and no illustrations to label. Instead, you are asked to know the answers to the questions and to know the material presented. Whether or not you have learned this material will be indicated by how well you do on the quizzes.

You will have your own specimen for dissection and will be graded individually on all parts of the Rat Lab. Your ability to follow directions and your skills in performing laboratory procedures can then be judged by the quality of your work. You must do your own work. You may consult your classmates or your instructor about information, sources, or directions, but you must do the dissection yourself. You are encouraged to study with other students, quizzing one another over the material, to prepare for the quizzes.

Contents

Goals

✓ Demonstrate, as a final exam project, the level of your laboratory skills

✓ Review subphylum Vertebrata, class Mammalia, and human anatomy and physiology

✓ Learn about the rat

Materials

preserved rat, *Rattus norvegicus*

dissection pan

dissection kit

pins

reference materials

mounted rat skeleton

plastic bag

Preparation for the Rat Lab

I. Preliminary procedures

- Read the *entire* Rat Lab before you come to class.

- Review Subsection 18.4 in your text.

- Plan to read and consult other texts as you work on the Rat Lab. You will not find in your text all the information you need to know to complete the dissections and the quizzes successfully. The books listed on page 222 are recommended; your instructor may suggest others. You may also find some information on the Internet. A search for "rat dissection" or "rat anatomy" may yield good results.

Suggested References for the Rat Lab

Hickman, Cleveland P., et al. *Integrated Principles of Zoology*. 14th ed. New York: McGraw-Hill, 2007.

Homberger, Dominique G., and Warren F. Walker. *Anatomy and Dissection of the Rat (Freeman laboratory separates in biology)*. 3rd ed. New York: W. H. Freeman, 1997.

Olds, Ronald John, and Joan R. Olds. *A Colour Atlas of the Rat: Dissection Guide*. Boca Raton, FL: CRC Press, 1988.

Schenk, Michael P., and David G. Smith. *Dissection Guide & Atlas to the Rat*. Englewood, CO: Morton Publishing Company, 2001.

Wingerd, Bruce D. *Rat Dissection Manual (Johns Hopkins Laboratory Dissections Series)*. 1st ed. Baltimore, MD: The Johns Hopkins University Press, 1988.

Wingerd, Bruce D. *Rat Anatomy and Dissection Guide*. Burlington, NC: Carolina Biological Supply, 2008.

II. Order of work

- This lab must be done in the order presented in the table of contents.

- The Muscle, Bone, and Skin Quiz; the Systems and Functions Quiz; and the Rat Master Quiz are your primary opportunities to earn points.

- While you are taking the Muscle, Bone, and Skin Quiz and the Systems and Functions Quiz, the quality of your dissection skill will be judged, and points will be awarded for your dissection work.

- You may take the quizzes at any time during the time allotted for the Rat Lab.

  □ You may study your dissected rat for as long as you wish before taking a quiz.

  □ You must take the quiz before you go on to the next section of the lab.

  □ Allow yourself enough time to complete the quiz. Once you begin a quiz, it counts, whether you finish it by the end of the class period or not.

- Plan ahead for the lab times.

  □ You will work on the Rat Lab in class from _____ to _____.

  □ Your instructor may announce additional times that the laboratory will be open for work on the Rat Lab. They include _____.

  □ The entire Rat Lab must be finished and the Score Sheet handed in by _____ AM/PM on _____.

III. Special notes

- On the Score Sheet are listed the point values of the various sections of the Rat Lab. After reading the Rat Lab, make a schedule to help you budget your time.

- When storing your rat overnight, place its internal structures in its body cavity and then wrap the entire organism in a damp paper towel. Place this in a plastic bag. Remove as much air as possible, close the bag tightly, and tie or zip it shut. Write your name on the bag with a pen or marker.

- When you are finished with a portion of the dissection and your work has been graded, you may wrap it in a paper towel and throw it away.

External Structures of the Rat

I. Learn the external structures of a rat well enough to do the following:

- Identify on your specimen each of the structures listed below.

  1. Pinnae

  2. Vibrissae (whiskers)

3. External nares (nostrils)

4. Upper eyelid

5. Lower eyelid

6. Nictitating membrane

7. Incisors

8. Forelimbs

9. Hind limbs

10. Cranial region

11. Thoracic region

12. Abdominal region

13. Teats (nipples)

14. Anus

15. Tail

16. Gender-specific structures

    a. Male: penis, urethral opening, and scrotal sacs (containing testes)

    b. Female: clitoris, urethral opening, vaginal opening, and vulva

17. Fur

- Know how each structure operates and what its functions are.
- Know the system to which each structure belongs.

II. Be able to answer the following questions about the rat's external structures:

- What do the openings at the pinnae lead to?
- Do the pinnae contain bone?
- What is the function of the vibrissae?
- How many teats are there? Are there teats found on males as well as females?
- How are the membranes around the rat's eye different from those around a human's eye?
- How do a rat's teeth differ from those of a human?
- Why do rats have such prominent incisors?
- What is the relationship (in position) between the upper and lower incisors?
- How is a rat's upper lip different from that of a human?
- Is the fur the same on all parts of the body?
- How is the surface of the tail different from the rest of the body?
- How many toes does a rat have on its forelimbs? On its hind limbs? What are the toes like?
- How many testes are there?
- What is the sex of your rat?

NOTE:
- You should make several quick diagrams of these external structures.
- As you do your research, jot down notes about pertinent facts you discover and list any questions you have.
- Use these diagrams and notes as a study guide when preparing for the quizzes.

Skinning the Rat

I. Removing the skin

- Place your rat in the dissection pan with its ventral side up.

- Pinch the skin in the thoracic region (over the sternum) enough to puncture it with the tip of your scissors. Carefully cut by continuing to raise the skin from the muscles and cut along the indicated lines (Figure RL-1) with your scissors, penetrating only into the subcutaneous layer. Do not cut into the muscles because you will need to observe them intact. Note that you will cut around each limb just proximal to each foot. You will also cut around the neck, the base of the tail, and the groin area, leaving that fur intact.

- After you have made all indicated cuts, use your forceps to pull the skin away from the muscles beneath. It should peel back as flaps if you patiently use your scissors and perhaps the probe to separate the skin from the muscles.

- Turn your rat over so that the dorsal side is up. Now complete the skin removal by pulling the skin away from the back in one piece. If all cuts were made properly, this should be possible.

II. Observing the skin

- Examine the skin that you have removed.

- Try to discriminate between the epidermis and the dermis.

- Distinguish, if possible, between underhair and the guard hairs.

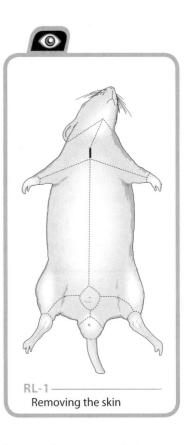

RL-1
Removing the skin

III. Saving and getting credit for the skin

- Wrap all the rat skin in a wet paper towel and save it until you are ready to take the Muscle, Bone, and Skin Quiz.

- As you take the Muscle, Bone, and Skin Quiz, your instructor will grade your rat skin. He will be looking for the following.

  □ Directions followed accurately

  □ Neatness

Bones and Muscles

I. Bones

- Learn the bones of the rat.

  □ Study carefully Figure RL-2.

  □ Study carefully the mounted rat skeleton in the classroom, if available, or other diagrams.

  □ Examine your skinned specimen to see how many of the bones or joints you can see or detect by touch.

- Note these facts about the rat skeleton.

  □ Know the structures in Figure RL-2. The structures you are asked to learn are basically the same structures you learned for humans.

  □ Note the major differences between human skeletons and rat skeletons.

II. Muscles

- Learn the muscles of the rat.

  □ Be able to identify the muscles listed in the chart on page 227 and illustrated in Figures RL-3 through RL-5 when they are pointed out.

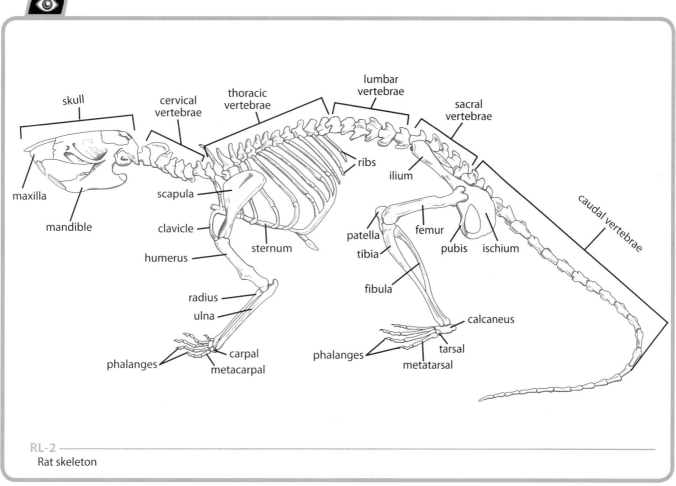

□ Know the meaning and application of the terms *origin* and *insertion*.

□ Be able to list the origin and insertion of each muscle.

□ Be able to demonstrate the function of each muscle.

• Observe these notes about rat muscles.

□ The muscles and structures you are asked to know are basically the same as the ones you learned for humans.

□ Muscle functions in the rat are often different from those in the human because of the difference between the body positions. The origins and insertions, however, are generally the same.

□ You will need to make no further cuts on your rat to be able to see all of the muscles indicated.

□ The superficial muscles shown in Figures RL-3 through RL-5 can be better defined by carefully separating them with your probe. Simply insert the probe under the loose edge of the muscle and slide along its margin. You can usually tell where one muscle separates from another by the direction of the fibers.

• After mastering the identification of the muscles in the chart and the figures, choose one hind leg and carefully remove the biceps femoris, gastrocnemius, and any other necessary underlying muscles to reveal the tibia, fibula, and femur, as well as the patella. Note the ligaments that hold the bones together at the knee and the Achilles tendon that joins the gastrocnemius to the calcaneus.

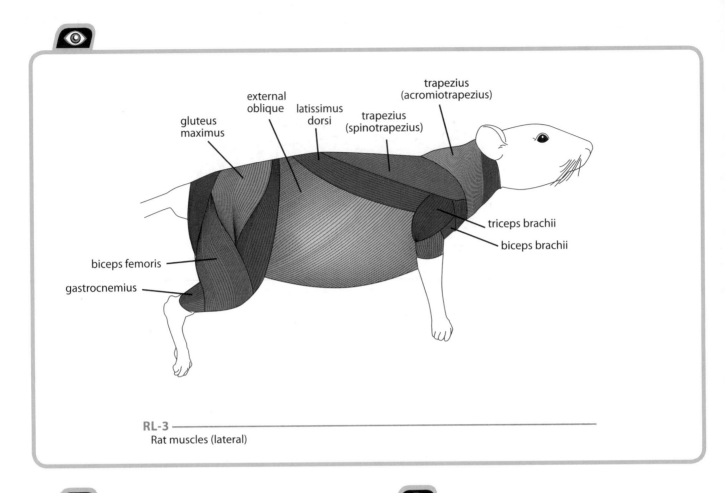

gluteus
maximus

external
oblique

latissimus
dorsi

trapezius
(spinotrapezius)

trapezius
(acromiotrapezius)

triceps brachii

biceps brachii

biceps femoris

gastrocnemius

RL-3

Rat muscles (lateral)

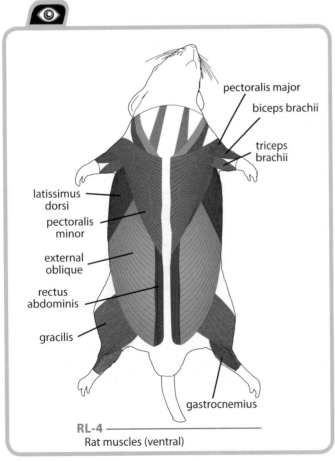

pectoralis major

biceps brachii

triceps
brachii

latissimus
dorsi

pectoralis
minor

external
oblique

rectus
abdominis

gracilis

gastrocnemius

RL-4

Rat muscles (ventral)

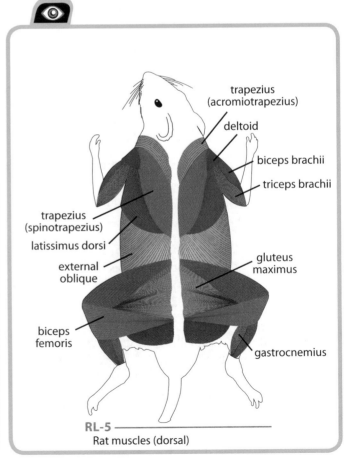

trapezius
(acromiotrapezius)

deltoid

biceps brachii

triceps brachii

trapezius
(spinotrapezius)

latissimus dorsi

external
oblique

gluteus
maximus

biceps
femoris

gastrocnemius

RL-5

Rat muscles (dorsal)

Muscles of the Rat

Name	Origin	Insertion	Function
trapezius (*acromiotrapezius*)	cervical and anterior thoracic vertebrae	scapula	pulls scapula inward, closer to ribs
trapezius (*spinotrapezius*)	posterior thoracic and anterior lumbar vertebrae	scapula	moves scapula up and backward
latissimus dorsi	thoracic and lumbar vertebrae	humerus	moves the humerus caudally
external oblique	muscles in region of last 9 or 10 ribs	linea alba and pubis	flexes body wall by compressing abdomen
gastrocnemius	femur	calcaneus	extends the foot
biceps femoris	ischium and sacral and caudal vertebrae	distal femur and proximal tibia	flexes the lower rear leg
gluteus maximus	ilium	femur	extends the thigh at the hip
triceps brachii	humerus and scapula	ulna	extends lower front leg
biceps brachii	scapula	proximal radius	flexes lower front leg
deltoid (*spinodeltoid*)	spine of scapular region	humerus	pulls scapula back and outward
pectoralis major	anterior sternum	proximal humerus	adducts front leg (draws it forward, toward chest)
pectoralis minor	posterior sternum	proximal humerus and scapula	adducts front leg (draws it forward, toward chest)
rectus abdominis	pubis	sternum	compresses abdomen
gracilis	pubis and ischium	tibia	pulls thigh forward

Muscle names in italics are used in some books and are included here for reference.

III. Review: You and your classmates can study the muscles and bones by pointing them out for each other and asking questions (about function, modification, origin, and so forth) until you have mastered the material.

Muscle, Bone, and Skin Quiz

I. About the quiz
- The Muscle, Bone, and Skin Quiz is a written fifteen-point quiz that includes specimens with numbered labels.
- You may take the quiz anytime you wish, and you may spend as much time on it as you need. Remember, though, that you must turn in any quiz at the end of the class period. (Average time is about fifteen minutes. Check the clock before you begin to make sure you have adequate time to complete the quiz.)

II. Taking the quiz
- When you come to obtain your copy of the quiz from the instructor, bring the following.
  - Your dissection pan, containing the skinned rat and the rat skin
  - Your Score Sheet
- While you take the quiz, your rat skin and muscle dissection will be graded and your score entered on the Score Sheet.
- When you have finished the quiz, hand it in and pick up your dissection pan and Score Sheet.

III. After the quiz
- **Do not discuss the content of the Muscle, Bone, and Skin Quiz with anyone.**
- Your score on the quiz will be given to you as soon as it is graded, and you will have a chance to review it at that time.
- You will have no further need of your rat skin and may discard it in a paper towel.

Opening the Rat's Body Cavity

NOTE:
- Be careful not to cut the internal organs as you make the incisions described below.
- Do not cut off limbs or any other structures unless you are instructed to do so. Careless cutting may cost you points.
- There are many ways to open the body cavity (coelom) of a rat. The method described below is recommended. It usually results in fewer damaged organs.

I. Place your rat in the dissection pan with its ventral side up.

II. Use your scissors to cut just through the muscle layers along the lines seen in Figure RL-6. It is best to make the longitudinal cut first and then the shorter transverse cuts.

III. After all of the cuts are made, fold the flaps back and pin them to the pan so that the organs are more easily seen.

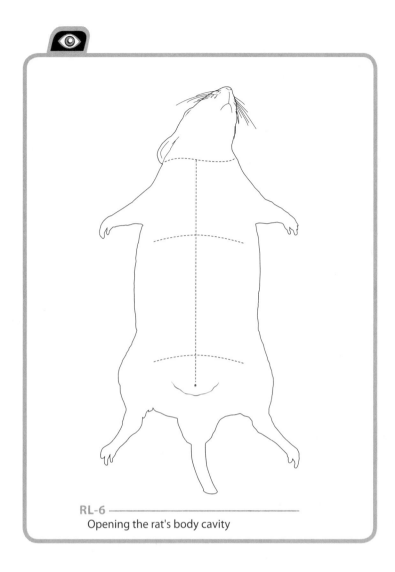

RL-6 ——————————————————————
Opening the rat's body cavity

Removing the Rat's Internal Systems

I. Do the following first.

- Identify all the internal structures that you can see.

- Mesenteries (thin, clear connective tissues with blood vessels running through them) hold the organs in place. Using a probe, loosen these mesenteries just enough so that all the internal viscera are visible.

- Before you continue cutting, locate all the following structures. Some of them are on the dorsal side of the body cavity, and you will need to use a probe to find them. **Do not cut any structures.**

1. Right atrium of heart
2. Left atrium of heart
3. Right ventricle of heart
4. Left ventricle of heart
5. Anterior venae cavae
6. Posterior vena cava
7. Aortic arch
8. Abdominal aorta
9. Larynx
10. Trachea
11. Lungs
12. Bronchi
13. Diaphragm
14. Esophagus
15. Stomach

16. Liver
17. Small intestine
18. Pancreas
19. Cecum
20. Colon (large intestine)
21. Rectum
22. Spleen
23. Thymus (if visible)
24. Kidneys
25. Ureters
26. Urinary bladder
27. Adrenal glands
28. Female: ovaries, vagina, and uterus (2 horns)
29. Male: testes, epididymis, and penis

II. Remove the circulatory system.

- It is easy to remove the heart, but identifying its structures after it has been removed from the body cavity can be difficult. While it is in its natural position, identify the structures in Figure RL-7.

- If you have a young rat, you will find a prominent thymus gland atop the heart. Remove it first.

- Be able to trace the blood flow through the rat's heart and to tell the oxygen content of the blood at all the various stages of the cardiac cycle of the rat.

- Remove the heart with as much of each blood vessel as possible (approximately 5 mm). The blood vessels are delicate and must be separated carefully from the surrounding tissues.

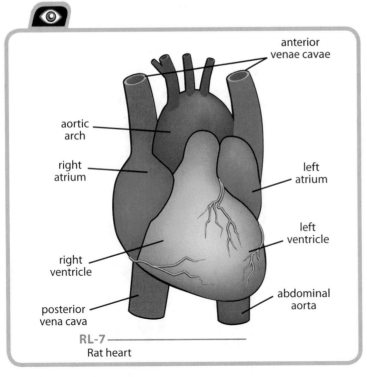

RL-7
Rat heart

- Wrap the circulatory system structures in a wet paper towel, and set them aside for further study and evaluation.

III. Remove the respiratory system.

- Identify the structures of the respiratory system (structures 9–13 on p. 230).

  □ Locate the lungs, found dorsal to the digestive system.

  □ The trachea is very short and connects the lungs.

  □ The bronchi are very short and may be hard to find if they are embedded in the lungs.

- Follow the trachea as near to the mouth cavity as possible. Include the larynx when you make the cut to remove this system.

  □ Do not cut the alimentary canal. The alimentary canal will be removed in another section.

  □ If the system is cut properly, the lungs will come out attached to each other.

  □ Mesenteries holding the trachea and the alimentary canal together should be removed.

- Study carefully the method the rat uses to breathe. Be able to answer the following questions.

  □ How do the rat's diaphragm and rib cage function in breathing?

  □ How does the lung tissue compare with the tissue of other rat organs?

- Wrap the respiratory system in a wet paper towel and save it for further study and evaluation.

RL-8
Rat ventral body cavity

IV. Remove the digestive system.

- Carefully cut the esophagus as close to the anterior as possible.
- Cut across the rectum, posterior to the end of the colon.
- Carefully separate any mesenteries connecting digestive organs to parts of the urogenital system and the vertebrae.
- The entire digestive system—with the liver, spleen, and pancreas intact—should now come out of the body cavity.
- Slowly tease the mesenteries with your probe so that the alimentary canal can be straightened.
- All accessory organs should remain attached to the alimentary canal.
- Know all the structures of the digestive system shown in Figure RL-8 and their functions. You should know the order in which food passes through these structures. The functions are the same as in humans.
- Be able to answer the following questions.

  □ How long is the alimentary canal?

  □ How long is it in relation to the length of the rat?

  □ Is this proportional to the relationship between human height and the length of the human alimentary canal?

        ◻ In regard to the rat and other vertebrates, what is the relationship between an animal's diet and the length of the intestine?

        ◻ How many lobes does the liver have?

        ◻ How is the structure of the esophagus different from that of the trachea?

        ◻ What human digestive structure is the equivalent of the rat's cecum?

V. Explore the urinary structures.

- Carefully locate and expose the urinary structures labeled in Figure RL-9 (male) or RL-10 (female). Do not remove the urinary structures but leave them in the rat body cavity.

- The ureters are sometimes hard to find due to their small size, but if you wiggle the kidneys it may be easier to see them.

- Note that the adrenal glands, atop the kidneys, are considered part of the endocrine system.

- Know all the structures of the urinary system and their functions. They are basically the same as those of humans.

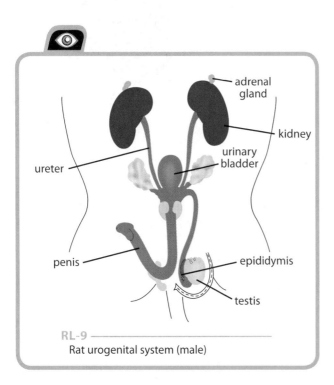

RL-9
Rat urogenital system (male)

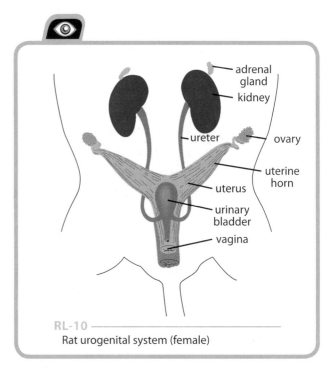

RL-10
Rat urogenital system (female)

VI. Explore the reproductive structures.

- Carefully locate and expose the reproductive structures labeled in Figure RL-9 or RL-10. Do not remove the reproductive structures but leave them in the rat body cavity.

- To access the testes, you will need to cut into the scrotal sac.

- Know all the structures of the reproductive system and their functions. They are basically the same as those of humans.

- You are responsible for both the male and female reproductive systems, so it would be good to trade rats with someone else who has the opposite sex as you prepare for the Rat Master Quiz.

Systems and Functions Quiz

I. About the quiz
- The Systems and Functions Quiz is a written fifteen-point quiz involving labeled specimens.
- Follow the instructions for taking the Muscle, Bone, and Skin Quiz, but this time present the dissected rat in your dissection pan with the organ systems displayed as in Figure RL-8.

II. After the quiz
- **Do not discuss the content of the Systems and Functions Quiz with anyone.**
- You will have no further need of your rat or its parts and should discard them in the trash, not down the drain.

Rat Master Quiz

I. About the quiz
- The Rat Master Quiz is a written sixty-point quiz (half of the total value of the Rat Lab) that does not involve specimens but does have drawings, objective questions, and essay questions.
- The quiz takes about thirty minutes. Before you ask for the quiz, make sure that you have enough time to complete it.
- To prepare for the quiz, be sure to do the following:
  - Read the supplemental materials suggested in the Rat Lab and know what you have read.
  - Know the structures mentioned in the Rat Lab and their functions.
  - Know the answers to all questions asked in the Rat Lab.

II. Taking the quiz
- When you are ready, ask your instructor for the quiz. You will need a blank sheet of paper on which to write your essay answers.
- When you hand in the Rat Master Quiz, attach your Score Sheet to it. You are now finished with the Rat Lab.
- **Do not discuss the content of the Rat Master Quiz with anyone.**

Laboratory Final Examination Score Sheet

I. Grading of dissection and taking quizzes

- Present this Score Sheet to your instructor when you take your Muscle, Bone, and Skin Quiz and when you take your Systems and Functions Quiz.

- Leave the Score Sheet with your dissected rat so that scores for your laboratory skills can be recorded.

- After you have taken the quiz and it has been graded, take the Score Sheet with your quiz score on it and keep it in a safe place. (You will lose points if you lose this sheet.)

II. Taking the Rat Master Quiz

- You must turn in this Score Sheet attached to the Rat Master Quiz.

- You must turn it in by _____ AM/PM on _____ to receive any credit for your Rat Lab.

- You need to turn in only this sheet with the Rat Master Quiz. You should not turn in the rest of the Rat Lab or any dissected rat parts.

Scores

Quizzes	Points Possible	Points Earned
• Muscle, Bone, and Skin Quiz	15	_____
• Systems and Functions Quiz	15	_____
• Rat Master Quiz	60	_____

Skills	Points Possible	Points Earned
• Skin	4	_____
• Circulatory System	5	_____
• Respiratory System	5	_____
• Digestive System	6	_____
• Urinary System	3	_____
• Reproductive System	3	_____
• General Skill	4	_____
Total 120		_____

Grade _____

Appendix A

Graphing Techniques

Constructing Graphs

When data are recorded in tables, it is difficult to see the relationship that exists between sets of numbers. To make trends and patterns easy to see, you will often put your data on a graph.

In experiments that lead you to search for a cause-effect relationship between two variables, you will cause one variable (the independent variable) to change and observe the effect on the second variable (the dependent variable). For experiments where you are unable to manipulate a variable, you may still graph the relationship between two variables. If you were to investigate how the level of glucose in the blood changes with time after a meal, time would be the independent variable, and blood glucose level would be the dependent variable. Traditionally, the independent variable is plotted on the x-axis of the graph, and the dependent variable is plotted on the y-axis.

As you construct your graph, choose a scale that will show the plotted points clearly. Do not make the graph so small that the data cannot be clearly seen or so large that the graph will not fit on a single sheet of paper. Pick a scale that will conveniently include the entire range of each variable. The scales on each axis do not have to be the same. For instance, the scale on the x-axis might be 1 hour for every line, while the scale on the y-axis could be 50 mg/100 mL for every line. Your scale should be easy to subdivide. Subdivisions of 1, 2, 5, and 10 are the most convenient.

Once you have decided which variable will be plotted on which axis and the scales that will be used, neatly label the name of each quantity and the numbers on each axis. The title of the graph should be printed at the top of the graph. If more than one line will be sketched on the same graph, include some key that identifies each line. Plot each of your data points by making small dots and circling them. Next, draw a smooth line that connects all the data points. Figure 1 illustrates these techniques.

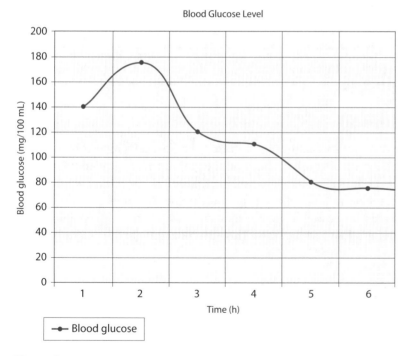

Blood Glucose Level	
Hours after eating (h)	Blood glucose (mg/100 mL)
1	140
2	175
3	120
4	110
5	80
6	75

Figure 1
Blood glucose level graph

In some cases, you will want to draw a straight line even though your data points do not fall precisely in a line. If this occurs, draw a line that shows the general relationship. Be sure to make the line go through the average values of the plotted points. The line in Figure 2a is incorrect because it lies above the cluster of points near the bottom of the graph and below the cluster of points at the top. Figure 2b shows the correct method of fitting a straight line to a series of points.

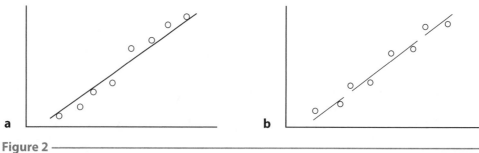

Figure 2 ───────────────────────────────────────
Incorrect method (a) and correct method (b) of fitting a straight line to a series of points

Interpreting Graphs

The shape of a graphed line tells much about the relationship between the variables. A straight line that rises from the origin indicates a direct relationship. A straight line that does not start at the origin shows that a linear relationship exists. A line that curves up (or down) from left to right indicates that the equation relating the two variables contains some exponent. A curved or straight line that is downward from left to right often describes an inverse relationship.

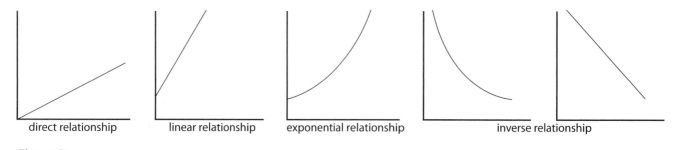

direct relationship   linear relationship   exponential relationship   inverse relationship

Figure 3 ───────────────────────────────────────
Typical graphs for different variable data relationships

    Graphs can be used to predict additional data points that have not been experimentally determined. Assuming that points between verified data points are correct because they fall on the graphed line is called *interpolation*. From the graph of blood glucose levels (Figure 1), it is reasonable to assume that the glucose level would be near 150 mg/100 mL at 2.5 hours. Extending the graphed line past the verified data points in either direction is called *extrapolation*. Extrapolations are usually indicated by dotted lines rather than by solid lines. The graph of blood glucose levels indicates that it would fall to 70 mg/100 mL at 7 hours. This extrapolation is reasonable, but it may not be totally accurate.

Appendix B

Laboratory Safety and First-aid Rules

Safety in the Laboratory

1. Attitude
   a. The biology laboratory must only be used for serious work.
   b. Never perform any unauthorized experiment.
   c. Always report any accident, injury, or incorrect procedure to your teacher at once.

2. Attire
   a. Wear safety glasses or goggles while working with chemicals, Bunsen burners, or anything that might get into your eyes.
   b. Wear a laboratory apron if you are working with chemicals or heated substances.
   c. Tie back long hair to keep it away from flames or open chemicals.
   d. Avoid wearing clothing with loose sleeves.
   e. Avoid wearing neckties.

3. Glassware
   a. Handle glassware and microscope slides carefully to minimize breakage.
   b. Report to your teacher any broken glassware or slides so that they can be placed into a designated container.
   c. Never use cracked or chipped glassware.

4. Handling chemicals
   a. Read labels on reagent bottles carefully.
   b. Avoid contaminating the chemicals. Do not return unused chemicals to bottles, insert your pipet into the bottle, or lay the stopper of a bottle down. If you must put a lid down, keep the inside surface from touching the surface of the table.
   c. Never taste anything unless specifically directed to do so.
   d. When smelling a substance, waft its vapor gently toward yourself.
   e. Never heat a chemical unless instructed to do so.
   f. Always add acid to water slowly when diluting acid solutions. Never add water to an acid.
   g. Keep combustible materials away from open flames.

5. Heating substances

   When heating substances in a test tube, do not point the mouth of the test tube toward anyone, and keep the tube moving in the flame.

6. Cutting
   a. Always use the instrument recommended in the lab instructions for the particular task.
   b. Handle scalpels, razor blades, probes, and scissors carefully.
   c. Always cut away from yourself, never toward yourself.

7. Live organisms
   a. Carefully follow all instructions for the handling of live organisms.
   b. No procedures that cause undue harm or discomfort should be performed in the laboratory. Some organisms may be sacrificed as part of a procedure, but they should not be treated cruelly.
   c. Thoroughly wash your hands with soap after handling any living organisms or cultures containing organisms.

8. Preparation

   Study your assignment before you come to the laboratory. Make sure that you understand EVERY procedure.

9. Cleanup

   a. Return all equipment and unused supplies to their designated places.

   b. Dispose of all trash and clean your work surface if necessary.

   c. Wash your hands before leaving the laboratory.

10. Safety equipment

    Know the locations of the fire extinguisher, safety shower, eyewash, fire blanket, first-aid kit, and MSDS binder.

First Aid in the Laboratory

1. Burns

   For burns from hot objects, flames, or chemicals, flush the area with cold water for several minutes.

2. Chemical spills

   a. On a laboratory desk

      1) If the material is not particularly volatile, toxic, or flammable, use an absorbent material that will neutralize the liquid. Then clean the area with soap and water.

      2) If the material is volatile, toxic, or flammable, extinguish all flames and evacuate the lab.

   b. On a person

      1) If it is a large area, remove all contaminated clothing while under the safety shower. Flood the affected body area for fifteen minutes. Obtain medical help immediately.

      2) If it is a small area, immediately flush the affected area with cold water for several minutes. Then wash the area with a mild detergent solution.

      3) If it is an acid, rinse the area with sodium bicarbonate solution; if it is a base, use boric acid solution.

      4) If the chemical splashes into the eyes, immediately wash the eyes in the nearest eyewash fountain for several minutes. Get medical attention.

3. Fire

   a. Smother a small fire with a cloth or beaker.

   b. Use a fire extinguisher for a larger fire.

   c. If a person's clothes are on fire, roll the person on the floor and use a fire blanket to extinguish the flames. The safety shower may also be used. DO NOT use a fire extinguisher on a person.

4. Swallowing chemicals

   Find out the specific substance ingested. Contact the Poison Control Center in your area immediately.

Life Processes Chart

Organism _____

Phylum _____ **Class** _____ **Genus** _____

Structure   **Notes**

Movement *(structures responsible for movement; types of movement)*

_____

_____

_____

_____

_____

Body Covering *(what covers the body; how it protects the animal)*

_____

_____

_____

_____

_____

Support *(structures responsible for support; what they are made of)*

_____

_____

_____

_____

_____

Nutrition *(structures of digestion; methods of ingestion; types of food; assimilation)*

_____

_____

_____

_____

_____

Respiration *(structures used in gas exchange for respiration)*

_____

_____

_____

_____

_____

Structure   **Notes**

Circulation *(structures responsible for internal movement of substances)*

_____

_____

_____

_____

_____

Excretion *(structures for the collection and elimination of soluble wastes)*

_____

_____

_____

_____

_____

Responses *(structures for receiving stimuli and for responses; level of responses)*

_____

_____

_____

_____

_____

Reproduction—Asexual *(structures for and types of asexual reproduction)*

_____

_____

_____

_____

_____

Reproduction—Sexual *(structures for sexual reproduction)*

_____

_____

_____

_____

_____

Other Notes *(habitat, size, range, unusual examples, etc.)*

_____

_____

_____

_____

_____

Life Processes Chart

Organism _____

Phylum _____ **Class** _____ **Genus** _____

Structure   **Notes**

Movement *(structures responsible for movement; types of movement)*

_____
_____
_____
_____
_____
_____

Body Covering *(what covers the body; how it protects the animal)*

_____
_____
_____
_____
_____

Support *(structures responsible for support; what they are made of)*

_____
_____
_____
_____
_____

Nutrition *(structures of digestion; methods of ingestion; types of food; assimilation)*

_____
_____
_____
_____

Respiration *(structures used in gas exchange for respiration)*

_____
_____
_____
_____
_____

Structure   Notes

Circulation *(structures responsible for internal movement of substances)*

_____

_____

_____

_____

_____

Excretion *(structures for the collection and elimination of soluble wastes)*

_____

_____

_____

_____

_____

Responses *(structures for receiving stimuli and for responses; level of responses)*

_____

_____

_____

_____

_____

Reproduction—Asexual *(structures for and types of asexual reproduction)*

_____

_____

_____

_____

_____

Reproduction—Sexual *(structures for sexual reproduction)*

_____

_____

_____

_____

_____

Other Notes *(habitat, size, range, unusual examples, etc.)*

_____

_____

_____

_____

name: _____

Life Processes Chart

Organism _____

Phylum _____ **Class** _____ **Genus** _____

Structure   **Notes**

Movement *(structures responsible for movement; types of movement)*

_____
_____
_____
_____
_____
_____

Body Covering *(what covers the body; how it protects the animal)*

_____
_____
_____
_____
_____
_____

Support *(structures responsible for support; what they are made of)*

_____
_____
_____
_____
_____
_____

Nutrition *(structures of digestion; methods of ingestion; types of food; assimilation)*

_____
_____
_____
_____
_____

Respiration *(structures used in gas exchange for respiration)*

_____
_____
_____
_____
_____

Structure	Notes

Circulation *(structures responsible for internal movement of substances)*

_____

_____

_____

_____

_____

Excretion *(structures for the collection and elimination of soluble wastes)*

_____

_____

_____

_____

_____

Responses *(structures for receiving stimuli and for responses; level of responses)*

_____

_____

_____

_____

_____

Reproduction—Asexual *(structures for and types of asexual reproduction)*

_____

_____

_____

_____

_____

Reproduction—Sexual *(structures for sexual reproduction)*

_____

_____

_____

_____

_____

Other Notes *(habitat, size, range, unusual examples, etc.)*

_____

_____

_____

_____

_____

Life Processes Chart

Organism _____

Phylum _____ **Class** _____ **Genus** _____

Structure   **Notes**

Movement *(structures responsible for movement; types of movement)*

_____

_____

_____

_____

_____

Body Covering *(what covers the body; how it protects the animal)*

_____

_____

_____

_____

_____

Support *(structures responsible for support; what they are made of)*

_____

_____

_____

_____

_____

Nutrition *(structures of digestion; methods of ingestion; types of food; assimilation)*

_____

_____

_____

_____

_____

Respiration *(structures used in gas exchange for respiration)*

_____

_____

_____

_____

_____

Structure	Notes

Circulation *(structures responsible for internal movement of substances)*

_____

_____

_____

_____

_____

Excretion *(structures for the collection and elimination of soluble wastes)*

_____

_____

_____

_____

_____

Responses *(structures for receiving stimuli and for responses; level of responses)*

_____

_____

_____

_____

_____

Reproduction—Asexual *(structures for and types of asexual reproduction)*

_____

_____

_____

_____

_____

Reproduction—Sexual *(structures for sexual reproduction)*

_____

_____

_____

_____

_____

Other Notes *(habitat, size, range, unusual examples, etc.)*

_____

_____

_____

_____

_____

name: _____

Life Processes Chart

Organism _____

Phylum _____ **Class** _____ **Genus** _____

Structure   **Notes**

Movement *(structures responsible for movement; types of movement)*

_____

_____

_____

_____

_____

Body Covering *(what covers the body; how it protects the animal)*

_____

_____

_____

_____

_____

Support *(structures responsible for support; what they are made of)*

_____

_____

_____

_____

_____

Nutrition *(structures of digestion; methods of ingestion; types of food; assimilation)*

_____

_____

_____

_____

_____

Respiration *(structures used in gas exchange for respiration)*

_____

_____

_____

_____

_____

Structure	Notes
Circulation (structures responsible for internal movement of substances)	
Excretion (structures for the collection and elimination of soluble wastes)	
Responses (structures for receiving stimuli and for responses; level of responses)	
Reproduction—Asexual (structures for and types of asexual reproduction)	
Reproduction—Sexual (structures for sexual reproduction)	
Other Notes (habitat, size, range, unusual examples, etc.)	

Life Processes Chart

name: _____

Organism _____

Phylum _____ **Class** _____ **Genus** _____

Structure   **Notes**

Movement *(structures responsible for movement; types of movement)*

_____
_____
_____
_____
_____

Body Covering *(what covers the body; how it protects the animal)*

_____
_____
_____
_____
_____

Support *(structures responsible for support; what they are made of)*

_____
_____
_____
_____
_____

Nutrition *(structures of digestion; methods of ingestion; types of food; assimilation)*

_____
_____
_____
_____

Respiration *(structures used in gas exchange for respiration)*

_____
_____
_____
_____
_____

Structure   **Notes**

Circulation *(structures responsible for internal movement of substances)*

_____

_____

_____

_____

_____

Excretion *(structures for the collection and elimination of soluble wastes)*

_____

_____

_____

_____

_____

Responses *(structures for receiving stimuli and for responses; level of responses)*

_____

_____

_____

_____

_____

Reproduction—Asexual *(structures for and types of asexual reproduction)*

_____

_____

_____

_____

_____

Reproduction—Sexual *(structures for sexual reproduction)*

_____

_____

_____

_____

_____

Other Notes *(habitat, size, range, unusual examples, etc.)*

_____

_____

_____

_____

_____

Life Processes Chart

Organism _____

Phylum _____ **Class** _____ **Genus** _____

Structure   **Notes**

Movement (structures responsible for movement; types of movement)

_____
_____
_____
_____
_____

Body Covering (what covers the body; how it protects the animal)

_____
_____
_____
_____

Support (structures responsible for support; what they are made of)

_____
_____
_____
_____
_____

Nutrition (structures of digestion; methods of ingestion; types of food; assimilation)

_____
_____
_____
_____
_____

Respiration (structures used in gas exchange for respiration)

_____
_____
_____
_____

Structure	Notes

Circulation (*structures responsible for internal movement of substances*)

_____

_____

_____

_____

_____

Excretion (*structures for the collection and elimination of soluble wastes*)

_____

_____

_____

_____

_____

Responses (*structures for receiving stimuli and for responses; level of responses*)

_____

_____

_____

_____

_____

Reproduction—Asexual (*structures for and types of asexual reproduction*)

_____

_____

_____

_____

_____

Reproduction—Sexual (*structures for sexual reproduction*)

_____

_____

_____

_____

_____

Other Notes (*habitat, size, range, unusual examples, etc.*)

_____

_____

_____

_____

_____

name: _____

Life Processes Chart

Organism _____

Phylum _____ **Class** _____ **Genus** _____

Structure   **Notes**

Movement *(structures responsible for movement; types of movement)*

_____

_____

_____

_____

_____

Body Covering *(what covers the body; how it protects the animal)*

_____

_____

_____

_____

_____

Support *(structures responsible for support; what they are made of)*

_____

_____

_____

_____

_____

Nutrition *(structures of digestion; methods of ingestion; types of food; assimilation)*

_____

_____

_____

_____

_____

Respiration *(structures used in gas exchange for respiration)*

_____

_____

_____

_____

_____

Structure	Notes

Circulation *(structures responsible for internal movement of substances)*

_____

_____

_____

_____

_____

Excretion *(structures for the collection and elimination of soluble wastes)*

_____

_____

_____

_____

_____

Responses *(structures for receiving stimuli and for responses; level of responses)*

_____

_____

_____

_____

_____

Reproduction—Asexual *(structures for and types of asexual reproduction)*

_____

_____

_____

_____

_____

Reproduction—Sexual *(structures for sexual reproduction)*

_____

_____

_____

_____

_____

Other Notes *(habitat, size, range, unusual examples, etc.)*

_____

_____

_____

_____

_____

Life Processes Chart

Life Processes Chart

Organism _____

Phylum _____ **Class** _____ **Genus** _____

Structure   **Notes**

Movement *(structures responsible for movement; types of movement)*

_____
_____
_____
_____
_____

Body Covering *(what covers the body; how it protects the animal)*

_____
_____
_____
_____
_____

Support *(structures responsible for support; what they are made of)*

_____
_____
_____
_____
_____

Nutrition *(structures of digestion; methods of ingestion; types of food; assimilation)*

_____
_____
_____
_____
_____

Respiration *(structures used in gas exchange for respiration)*

_____
_____
_____
_____
_____

Structure	Notes

Circulation (structures responsible for internal movement of substances)

_____

_____

_____

_____

_____

Excretion (structures for the collection and elimination of soluble wastes)

_____

_____

_____

_____

_____

Responses (structures for receiving stimuli and for responses; level of responses)

_____

_____

_____

_____

_____

Reproduction—Asexual (structures for and types of asexual reproduction)

_____

_____

_____

_____

_____

Reproduction—Sexual (structures for sexual reproduction)

_____

_____

_____

_____

_____

Other Notes (habitat, size, range, unusual examples, etc.)

_____

_____

_____

_____

_____

Life Processes Chart

Organism _____

Phylum _____ **Class** _____ **Genus** _____

Structure   **Notes**

Movement *(structures responsible for movement; types of movement)*

_____
_____
_____
_____
_____

Body Covering *(what covers the body; how it protects the animal)*

_____
_____
_____
_____
_____

Support *(structures responsible for support; what they are made of)*

_____
_____
_____
_____
_____

Nutrition *(structures of digestion; methods of ingestion; types of food; assimilation)*

_____
_____
_____
_____
_____

Respiration *(structures used in gas exchange for respiration)*

_____
_____
_____
_____

Structure	Notes
Circulation *(structures responsible for internal movement of substances)*	
_____	_____
_____	_____
_____	_____
_____	_____
_____	_____
Excretion *(structures for the collection and elimination of soluble wastes)*	
_____	_____
_____	_____
_____	_____
_____	_____
_____	_____
Responses *(structures for receiving stimuli and for responses; level of responses)*	
_____	_____
_____	_____
_____	_____
_____	_____
_____	_____
Reproduction—Asexual *(structures for and types of asexual reproduction)*	
_____	_____
_____	_____
_____	_____
_____	_____
_____	_____
Reproduction—Sexual *(structures for sexual reproduction)*	
_____	_____
_____	_____
_____	_____
_____	_____
_____	_____
Other Notes *(habitat, size, range, unusual examples, etc.)*	
_____	_____
_____	_____
_____	_____
_____	_____
_____	_____